GCSE
PE
for Edexcel

Tony Scott

Edexcel
Success through qualifications

Heinemann

D1461062

Second edition

This book is dedicated to my wife Louise, for her constant support, strength and encouragement, especially in the last two years, and to the late Jonathan Levi, Graeme Alexander, Emma Bateman, Alex Gimson, the staff and all the team on C9, without whom I would not have been able to write this book.

Heinemann Educational Publishers
Halley Court, Jordan Hill, Oxford OX2 8EJ
a division of Reed Educational and Professional
Publishing Ltd.
Heinemann is a registered trademark of Reed
Educational and Professional Publishing Ltd.

OXFORD MELBOURNE AUCKLAND KAMPALA
JOHANNESBURG BLANTYRE GABORONE
IBADAN PORTSMOUTH (NH) USA CHICAGO

British Library Cataloguing in Publication Data
A catalogue record for this book is available from the British Library

10 – digit ISBN: 0 435506 37 4
13 – digit ISBN: 978 0 435506 37 7

Designed and typeset by Artistix, Thame, Oxon
Cover design by Brian Melvin, Big Red Hat Design
Illustrations by Catherine Ward Illustrations
Printed and bound in China by CTPS

Acknowledgements
The author would like to thank the following for their help during the writing and production of this book: Alistair Christie, Helen Reilly; Jane Tyler, Rob Bircher, Stephani Havard and Sue Walton of Heinemann; Roger Beard of Edexcel; Kevin Hoare, Ian Smithson, Matt Stevens and Sam Jones at Finchley High School for their interest and support, and Derek Rosenberg for his faith in me.

The publishers would like to thank the following for permission to reproduce copyright material: Knight Features for the cartoon on p. 7, PEANUTS copyright © 1999 United Feature Syndicate, Inc., reproduced by permission; Health Development Agency for the diagrams on pp. 41 and 42, reproduced with permission; The Daily Mail/Atlantic Syndication Partners for the Mahood cartoon on p. 28, and the extract on p. 21.

The publishers would like to thank the following for permission to use photographs: Severn/Allsport, p. 8; Simon Bruty/Allsport, p. 9; Colorsport, p. 10; Aubrey Washington/Empics, p. 11; Empics/Witters, p. 12 (left); Matthew Aston/Empics, p. 12 (right); Gareth Boden, p. 13; Colorsport, p. 13 (top), Empics/Michael Steel, p. 14; J. Gichigi/Allsport, p. 16 (top); Empics, p. 17 (bottom); Neal Simpson/Empics, p. 18 (top); M. Steele/Empics, p. 18 (bottom); Neal Simpson/Empics, p. 20; Colorsport, p. 21; Todd Warshaw/Allsport, p. 26; D. Worthy/Empics, p. 30 (top); Robinson/Empics, p. 30 (bottom); P. Rondeau/Allsport, p. 31 (top); N. Simpson/Empics, p. 31 (bottom); Colorsport, p. 32; D. Cannon/Allsport, p. 33; Neal Simpson/Empics, p. 34; Empics, p. 35; Colorsport, p. 36; SPL, p. 38; Rex Features, p. 39; Gary Prior/Allsport, p. 44; Solo Syndication, p. 45; SPL, p. 47; Colorsport, p. 48; Mike Egerton/Empics, p. 49; Spectrum Colour library, p. 50 (both); Empix, p. 52; Frank Spooner, p. 53; Gichigi/Allsport, p. 54; SPL, p. 61; Neal Simpson/Empics, p. 62; Simon Fraser/SPL, p. 63; Yann Arthus Bertrand/Impact, p. 64 (bottom); P. Phillips/SPI, p. 64 (top), Dr Nurti/SPL, p. 65; CNRI/SPL, p. 66 (top); David Scharf/SPL, p. 66 (bottom); SPL, p. 67; Bubbles, p. 74; A. Heading/Empics, p. 76; S. Cruz/Allsport, p. 78; Alan Edwards, p. 79; Al Bellol/Allsport, p. 80; Karl Weatherly/Allsport, p. 82; Solo Syndication, p. 83; Phil O'Brien/Empics, p. 84; Neal Simpson/Empics, p. 85; J. McDonald/Allsport, p. 89 (bottom), J. Herbert/Allsport, p. 89 (top); Photofusion, p. 90; D. Campione/SPL, p. 93; Michael Steele/Empics, p. 100; Peter Arkell/Impact, p. 101; BSIP/SPL, p. 102 (bottom); Damien Lovegrove/SPL, p. 104; Rupert Conant/Impact, p. 105; Tek Image/Science Photo, p. 110; Colorsport, p. 117; Michael Steele/Empics, p. 120; Gail Devers/Allsport, p. 122; T. Marshall/Empics, p. 127; Matthew Aston/Empics, p. 131; M. Egerton/Empics, p. 135; Empics, p. 136; Prince Naseem/Action Images, p. 139; Action images, p. 140; John Cole/Impact, p. 142; Ian Wilson/Capital Pictures, p. 143; Empics/Aubrey Washington, p. 144; A. Washington/Empics, p. 145 (left); Ashton/Empics, p. 145 (right); T. Honan/Empics, p. 146 (left); M. Egerton/Empics, p. 146 (right); Andrew Redington/Allsport, p. 147; Sporting Pictures, p.148; Allsport, p. 149; Barry Coobs/Empics, p. 151; Colorsport, p. 152. All other photos by Alan Edwards. The publishers would like to thank all those staff and students of Finchley Catholic High School who took part in the photo shoot for this book.

The publishers would like to thank Action-Plus (canoeing picture), Alan Edwards (dance, basketball and trampolining pictures), Image Bank (swimming picture) and Pictor International (high jump picture) for permission to reproduce the cover photographs.

The publishers have made every effort to trace copyright holders. However, if any material has been incorrectly acknowledged, we would be pleased to correct this at the earliest opportunity.

Contents

Introduction

This book has been written for the Edexcel GCSE Physical Education specification.

All the different parts of the specification are covered in this book, but they have been re-arranged into a course for you to follow. The book has been written in such a way as to try to make the course interesting and as easy as possible for you to learn what you need to know and understand. When you have finished you should be able to relate the different parts of the specification to one another to show an understanding of how all the parts of the course fit together in Physical Education.

How the book is set out

The first units in the book are concerned with the practical aspects of the course. In section one, you are shown how to set targets for your first practical activity and how to decide on ways to reach them. You are then asked to set your first short-term goals. You should perform this same exercise before each practical activity. There will be four coursework marks that will build together as you progress through the course, to give you your final coursework total out of 50.

The next units are all concerned with the analysis of performance, in which you will be expected to analyse your own and others' performance. You will be shown in detail how to do this, which you can then practise in your practical activities. You will be expected to set a target for your analysis of performance grade in a similar way to that which you did for the practical activity.

The second and subsequent sections cover theoretical aspects of the course, which come under the title 'Factors affecting participation and performance', starting with the reasons why people take part in sport and physical education. The book then looks at the wider areas and the many factors that affect performance, ranging from the ordinary sportsperson to champions in sport.

The section on 'Applied anatomy and physiology' covers Section C of the specification and in the examination the emphasis for this section will be very much on the *application* of your knowledge. In order to do this, however, you will need to have what might be called 'underpinning knowledge' about anatomy and physiology; if you do not have the knowledge, you will not be able to apply it! You may have covered some of the facts about anatomy and physiology already in Science, but not necessarily in a Physical Education or sporting context, and that is why this underpinning knowledge is covered in this book. Information about applied anatomy and physiology is found throughout this book, not just in the Applied anatomy and physiology section.

For example, in order to understand the applied work on blood pressure and the affects of exercise, training and stress, it will help to have knowledge of the heart, the blood and the blood vessels. Therefore the work on the heart forms the *underpinning knowledge* of the cardiovascular system, which is the most important aspect of Health Related Exercise. The underpinning knowledge will also help you to understand the importance of the Personal Exercise Programme (PEP), how to plan it, what to include and how to evaluate it when you have performed it. You should use this knowledge whether watching or playing to enhance your ability to analyse your own and others' performance.

Revision

There are two pages at the end of the book to help with your revision. Numerous television programmes, videos and CD-ROMS that can reinforce your revision work are also available.

Following this book should prepare you well for Edexcel A/S and A level courses in Physical Education if you decide to continue with PE.

Good luck with your GCSE course!

Target setting for practical activities

In this first lesson, you will learn about target setting. Although you may have come across this in other subjects or during your Key Stage 3 programme, it will be important in your GCSE Physical Education course as it will help you to set out ways to get the best possible results.

If you are taking the full course, you will take four different practical activities. In the short course, you will only take two.

At the end of the coursework and during a final assessment at the end of the whole two-year course, you will be assessed by your teacher in each of these practical activities, both in your ability to apply your individual skills and in a game or competitive situation. A mark out of 10 will be allocated, then compared to either criteria or the **profile** laid down by the examination board (Edexcel). This information is presented in a large book called a Coursework Guide. Your teacher will have a copy of the guide and may photocopy the parts that you will be marked against – for example, in basketball. You may not get the same mark for each aspect of the profile. In the basketball example you may score in the 7–8 band for control, but in the 5–6 band for the other aspects, such as the lay-up and jump shot. This will *probably* mean that you will be called a high 6, but would not merit a 7.

This box shows an example of target setting for basketball.

Example

1 I think that I am in the 5–6 band now.
2 In order to improve to the 7–8 band, I need to work on:
   - dribbling – become effective with either hand
   - passing – improve my ability to use variety and deception and learn to signal effectively and with good timing
   - lay-up – improve my drive from my weaker side but I may lay up with my stronger hand
   - jump shot – improve to a very effective standing jump shot; landing in the correct position
   - game – improve my ability to exploit openings and threaten opponents by scoring and/or assisting.
3 In order to do this, I will:
   - work hard and pay special attention to these aspects in the lessons
   - attend basketball practices.

Target setting in this way should be completed before the start of each practical activity.

Tasks

a Study the profile for your first activity and work out what mark you would expect to get if you took the examination now.

b Work out the points you think you should work on in order to improve to the next grade or band. List ways to achieve this.

Key terms

- **competitive situation**
- **Coursework Guide**
- **profile**
- **skills**
- **target setting**

Target setting for analysis of performance

Whether you are doing a full or short course GCSE in PE, you will be examined on your ability to **analyse** your own and others' **performance** and suggest ways of improving. It is important to set targets in this area too. Although you may practise all your practical activities, you will be given your final grade based on the one you do best. The analysis of performance is worth 10 per cent of your final mark.

Performance analysis skills

These are the skills on which you will be tested in analysing performance:

1   Your knowledge of the rules and regulations of the game including, at the highest level, your ability to apply them as a player, referee, umpire, judge, or other official. You will be tested on your knowledge of terminology used in the activity: 'birdie' in golf, or the names of tactical formations in team games.

2   You will be asked to **observe** and analyse a performance.

3   Then you will be expected to evaluate and measure the performance against what it should look like at its best. This is called knowledge of the **perfect model**. You will need to explain the perfect model and identify both strengths and weaknesses in your own and other students' performances.

4   You will learn a lot about strategies, tactics and practices that can help to improve performances, and **training**. You will have to show that you can plan strategies and practices and show your knowledge of training methods and how they can improve your own and others' performances through your Personal Exercise Programme (PEP).

5   You will need to show that you understand the role of leadership in your activity.

Task

Complete your work for your target setting in the analysis of performance in the same way that you did your target setting for the practical activity on page 6. You will need to complete these statements:

● I think my grade is now at level …

● I want to improve to level …

● In order to reach my targets I need to improve in the following areas: …

● I will achieve this by …

PEANUTS copyright © 1999 United Feature Syndicate, Inc. Reproduced by permission.

Key terms

● analyse
● observe
● the perfect model
● performance
● rules
● strengths and weaknesses
● terminology
● training

An introduction to analysis of performance

Part two of the course includes all the practical aspects. The analysis of performance part of the course is known as part 2B (part 2 because it comes in the practical part of the course and B because it comes after 2A, the practical coursework, and before 2C, the final practical assessment).

You may have had some practice at analysing performance during Key Stage 3, but it was probably called 'evaluation' and/or 'planning'. If you choose to study Physical Education at AS and A level, this will again be part of your course and it will have a similar marking system.

Five areas of analysis

For your analysis of performance, you will gain marks out of four in each of five areas of knowledge and interpretation (as listed on page 7). In the first area, regarding rules and their role in sport, you might demonstrate your knowledge by officiating a game or judging a competition, or you may be asked questions while others are playing or performing. (In some sports, rules may also be called 'regulations'.) In this same area, you can show your understanding of the terminology used in your sport by using the correct terms when discussing a performance. For example, if you refer to a drop shot in a racket game, this is using correct terminology. Likewise, in hockey you might use the term 'reverse stick', or in football you might refer to the channels. Using the correct terminology shows that you have the basis of understanding required to carry out an analysis in your sport.

In the second area, while observing others perform, you will be expected to examine their performance in detail, that is, to analyse the performance. A variety of ways are shown later of how you might do this.

The third area requires you to **evaluate** the performance against what you think it should look like – the perfect model – and comment on its strengths and weaknesses. You may not be able to perform it yourself, but you need to know how it *should* be done! Do not be tempted only to find faults; you can show your knowledge by pointing out the strengths of a performance – what is good about it. You may also be asked to comment on your own performance.

After you have made your evaluation, based on your analysis, you will have to demonstrate your decision-making capabilities by planning how the performance can be improved. To do this, you will need to have a knowledge of practices to improve the performer's skills, of tactics and strategies to improve team play, and of fitness training. Fitness training should be based upon your own Personal Exercise Programme (PEP), designed to improve your own fitness for this activity.

In some sports good technique is vital

Finally, you will be expected to show and comment on the ways that leadership can enhance performance in sport, the role of the captain and how the captain can influence their team and individual players. You should have a knowledge of how different coaches work to get the best from their team, and of the role of the manager.

Improving your analysis skills

You can practise and improve your ability to analyse in many ways. Some ideas are shown in the following pages. Many students become quite expert in this area of the course. Coaching awards or officiating awards in your best activity will almost certainly help you to do well in this part of the course.

Points to remember

Some simple points to remember to start with are:

1   If you do not hear the questions properly, ask the teacher or examiner to repeat them.

2   You will not be expected to give an analysis/evaluation straight away. Watch the performer or the game for a few minutes.

3   Take your time and think carefully before giving your answers.

When analysing a performance (and teaching or coaching), there are models from which to work. One such model was devised by Frank et al. ('et al.' means 'and others') in 1983 and it is shown at the bottom of this page.

In team games tactics are vital

Key terms

● **analysis and evaluation**
● **rules**
● **skills practices**
● **strengths and weaknesses**
● **tactics**
● **terminology**
● **the perfect model**
● **training**

Coaching model and definitions that may be useful

(or you could produce your own)

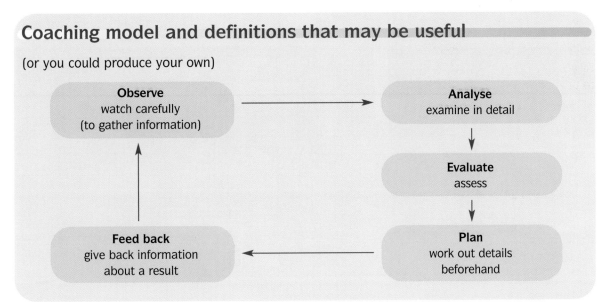

Observe
watch carefully
(to gather information)

Analyse
examine in detail

Evaluate
assess

Feed back
give back information
about a result

Plan
work out details
beforehand

Observational skills

The diagram on the previous page shows that the first thing to do in order to analyse a performance is to observe it, or watch it carefully so that you can gather information.

Getting the best view

To gather information, or the best information, we need to observe from the best position. In order to do this we must consider quite a few points before we even start.

This is where a sound knowledge of the activity will help. For example, a golf professional will view a player they are coaching from more than one angle before they make any comment about the shots. They will also want to observe several shots before they are satisfied with the information they have obtained.

A good coach will also note immediately whether a player is right- or left-handed because this will affect the position from where they observe. A good player should also note if an opponent is left-handed, or left-footed. Some football coaches in the Premier League may watch the game from the grandstand in

order to get the best view, others may want to be at the pitch side in order to be close to the play. Alternatively, some may watch from the grandstand and then come down to the pitch side at some point during the game.

To summarize

To get the best view we may need to observe from:

- above
- below
- the side
- behind
- in front
- more than one position.

We may also need more than one viewing and may need to consider:

- conditions (distance, weather, inside, outside)
- whether the performer is right-handed or left-handed.

And most important of all:

- where to stand for safety!

The Arsenal coaching staff observe the game from the dugout. Is this the place to get the best view?

Concentration

Observation and information gathering need our full concentration. If there are other activities going on at the same time, our concentration may wander from the job in hand.

Breaking down skills

It is important, where possible, to break down skills into component parts. In most sports, there is a recognized way of doing this. In swimming, for example, the strokes can be broken down into:

- body position
- leg action
- arm action
- breathing
- timing.

> ### Task 1
>
> Choose a sport and then choose a skill from that sport. Now break down the skill, so that you can observe the performance in small parts.

Invasion games

In invasion games, we might break the game down into attack and defence and then concentrate on one of these first.

An example might be to look at the particular defensive formation of our opponents. We might then look at our own attacking formation to see if we are using the best methods to break down our opponents' defence. The score in the game, or some other written information, might give us a good indication as to whether we are being successful or not.

Racket games

In racket games, we might look at what are known as forced and unforced errors. A forced error occurs when our opponent makes a winning shot that we cannot get back, while an unforced error might be a poor shot from us – a service fault is a good example.

> ### Task 2
>
> Choose an invasion game and devise a table to record the successful passes and unsuccessful passes of each player in the team.

Focus

Breaking down skills in this way will help us to focus on one particular aspect at a time, and after breaking it down we can then build it up again.

This picure shows good timing of breathing and arm action in the front crawl

Key terms

- best view
- break down skills
- concentration
- focus
- observe

Experience

It will help us to analyse if we have some experience in the activity or game. People generally do well at analysing activities in which they are most proficient. Most top coaches have experience and have played to a high standard in the activity in which they coach. Many coaches have experience of different roles in their sport – they may have been a team captain, for example.

Practice

It also helps to practise as much as possible, both in your main sport and in others too. This helps to develop your ability to spot faults, but also to notice the good aspects of a performance or skill.

Learning from others

We can learn a lot about analysing by watching and listening to others who are both experienced and practised in the art. There are of course many professionals who appear on television or who write columns for newspapers and are paid a lot of money to analyse their sport.

Video

It is now possible to make use of video recordings to learn, practise and improve your ability to analyse performances. You can do this by recording from a television programme (from which there are many to choose) and studying the various analysts, or by watching videos that are made for specific sports – again there are many available. CD-ROMs and the Internet are other resources that are available. Finally, it is now quite easy to make your own video of yourself or your friends and study the performances in some depth.

Task 2

With a partner, or in your GCSE group, make a short video of the sport you are taking part in at the moment. Then write a report as if you were writing a column for a sports paper. Make sure you analyse the performance.

Task 1

Make a list of five sports and then name one sports analyst for each of them. For example, soccer – Alan Hansen (or Martin O'Neill).

Celtic's manager Martin O'Neill was a very successful international player, a successful manager for Leicester City and an excellent analyst on television

Knowledge of the perfect model

Playing experience has already been mentioned as an important factor in being able to analyse performance. It should help you to develop a knowledge of what the skill or activity should look like when performed perfectly. However, it is possible to have this knowledge without being able to perform the perfect model yourself. This knowledge may come from playing without being able to perform at the highest level, watching others, reading/studying the sport in depth, or it may be gained from being with sportspeople who have achieved at the highest level and listening and learning from them.

Task 3

Choose the skill you perform best from any sport you know. Describe, in writing or by talking to your partner, exactly how to perform that skill to perfection.

Top sportspeople are able to demonstrate the perfect model in their sport

Keeping the arms close in to the body allows this trampolinist to spin quickly

Notational techniques

There are two ways in which we can gain information. One is by watching carefully and the other is by making written notes of what happens during the competition, match, or game. This is more of a description, which can be used later. For more details on this see page 19.

Knowledge of sports mechanics

This is a knowledge of what should be the correct scientific way to perform the skills to make them work best. An example might be in trampolining or gymnastics. In order for a performer to make a twisting movement, they will have to revolve around the longitudinal (vertical) axis. The more their arms and legs are wrapped into their body, the quicker they will turn (see the photo at the top of this page).

Key terms

- experience
- notational techniques
- practice
- sports mechanics
- the perfect model

Mental approach

Sports psychology is now recognized as a very important aspect in the improvements in present-day sports performance, and many teams and individuals make use of the help that a sports psychologist can give them. Although during your analysis of performance you might make points about the mental approach of players or teams, you will not be expected to have a detailed knowledge in this area, which will form part of your course if you go on to take A level Physical Education with Edexcel.

So the next question might be: What should we look for concerning the mental approach of players when observing (getting information on) a performance? The answer might be a combination of the 14 considerations that follow.

Maurice Green has a very strong mental approach to his running

1 What are the good points?

It seems that it is easier to criticize than it is to praise because many students' first comments are about poor performance rather than about good points. Most performances have good points, and although sometimes it might be difficult to find them, it is a good place to start. Although the mental aspects of performance are mostly to be found at A level, it would help the performer's confidence if at least some good points were made about what they are trying to do.

Task 1

Observe a partner's performance. Report only the good points to them.

2 The faults?

Just as there are good points about most poor performances, there are also areas that can be improved in most good performances. It may just be that they are more difficult to find. There may also be a number of faults about a performance that could be areas for improvement and you need to note as many as you can. You need to develop the skill of deciding which one the performer should work on first to bring about improvement.

Task 2

Observe a partner's performance and work out the faults. Then list them in order of importance. Put the one needing most improvement at the top of the list.

3 What are the results like?

This does not necessarily mean the result at the end of the game, match or competition. It could mean the result at the end of a skill, e.g. a table tennis service. If a player serves and it is legal and they win the point regularly, does the service need to be practised or improved? It might be that you decide that it does need to be improved because at a higher level an opponent would be able to deal quite easily with that service.

At the highest level it would be a brave coach who criticized world 200 and 400 metres champion Michael Johnson's technique when he has literally led the field for such a long time.

A practice can be devised to improve a particular skill

Task 3

Observe your partner repeating a skill, e.g. a service in a racket game. Watch the skill 20 times and decide how successfully the skill is performed. For example, 5/20 = needs to practise hard, 18/20 = very good.

4 Ways to improve skills

Finding the faults is only part of the job. Perhaps the more difficult part is having the knowledge to improve those skills, and being able to devise ways of doing so. This will form part of your assessment.

It might be that players can perform skills well when there is no opposition but not so well in a game. Therefore a practice must be used, where opposition is introduced in order to improve the players' skills under some pressure.

Task 4

a Observe your partner performing a particular skill. Now observe them in a game situation and concentrate on that same skill. Assess how successfully the skill is performed in each situation.

b Devise a practice to improve this skill.

Skills can be improved by using good practice drills

Key terms

● **faults**
● **good points**
● **results**
● **skills**
● **sports psychology**

5 Are the players fit?

You will be expected to have a knowledge of practices and training. **Fitness** could have a bearing on how well a player performs, especially in the later stages of a game, match, or competition, so noting this during an analysis would be important. It is also important to know how players can improve their fitness and you can use your knowledge from your own PEP to help with this.

Task 5

Choose a sport. Describe to your partner how to improve fitness in this sport.

6 Fitness testing

It is possible to test certain aspects of fitness and during your analysis you might refer to some of these tests. You could suggest how tests might be used in a fitness-training programme for the particular sport you are analysing. One example of a fitness test is a grip test for strength.

Fitness training is an important part of many sports

Combat sports need a wide range of fitness types, including grip strength

7 Capitalizing on good skills:

Have the player or players got good skills?

Having decided on the strengths of players, it may be possible to emphasize these within the game situation, or it may be possible to use players' other natural assets to the best possible advantage (see pages 35–7).

In a game like basketball, we would expect to see the tall players rebounding from the backboard, not dribbling the ball up the court, with the small players rebounding against tall defenders. In tennis, players with 'big serves' use their serves to advantage. Racket players may have favourite shots, for example, the drop shot.

Task 6

Name your best sport and then describe how you can use your best skill to advantage, e.g. your service in table tennis.

8 Hiding weaknesses

Just as you may find faults in a player and then find ways of improving them, it is also possible to hide faults in player and team performance. Many coaches work on players' strengths and simply try to hide the weaknesses. It is then up to the opposition to find and expose them. In games where players may use either foot or either hand, one hand or foot may be weaker than the other. Likewise, in games where players may use both forehand and backhand shots, one may be stronger or weaker than the other.

These weaknesses cannot be overcome in a short practice session, therefore ways may be devised to hide them. An example might be to play a player on the side of the pitch or court where they can use the strength of their strong foot and hide the weakness of the weak one. In the case of forehand and backhand shots, players may try to give themselves more room on their strong side.

Football strikers are always looking for any weaknesses in a goalkeeper

Task 7

In a given sport which a group may take part in, name your biggest weakness and describe to your partner how you will try to hide it in a game situation. Now play against your partner in this game. How easy is it to hide your weakness?

9 Exposing weaknesses

Finding a weakness in an opponent or team is only part of the job. Exposing it is another! A player with a weakness can be 'overplayed' in that area. This means that they will be given little room to work on the strong side and tempted to work on the weaker side. In the case of someone with a weak forehand or backhand, the player may hide the fault when they are in possession or have service. However, the opponent can expose the weakness when *they* have the service, or they can set up the play to expose the weakness in a later shot.

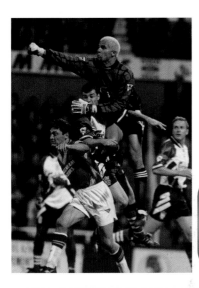

At the highest levels of sport it is difficult to hide a weakness for long

Task 8

Your partner will have explained their weakness in the given game in the last task. Now play the game again and try to find a way to expose their weakness.

Key terms

- exposing weaknesses
- fitness testing
- fitness-training programme
- hiding faults
- natural assets

10 Is the teamwork good?

Teamwork may not be so important in certain activities nor in individual activities such as swimming, trampolining and gymnastics, but in many of the other areas it is necessary to gain information on this.

How the players gel together is a major part of the success of many teams, and this includes racket games where doubles and mixed doubles are played. Working together, understanding the tactics and assisting other team members can often make up for deficiencies in other areas.

Task 9

Look for an example from the media that mentions the teamwork of players or a team, and report this to your partner.

Players need to work together to get the best results

11 Getting our tactics right

In sport at the lower levels there may be no **tactics**, while in sport at the highest levels a great deal of time and effort is given to devising team or player tactics. Tactics might be changed in order to deal with particular opposition. Indeed, in the football Premiership,

Tennis partners can discuss tactics between points

clubs might actually change their team if they are playing against a certain opposition, because they know (or think they know) what tactics the opposition will use.

However, a team will generally devise their tactics according to the players they have available. In professional sport, on the other hand, a club might actually seek to buy a player to fit into the team's tactics and hopefully improve the team's performance.

12 What are the opponent's tactics?

In professional sport, coaches or **scouts** will attend the games of future opponents in order to gather information before devising tactics to use in future games. This also helps them to decide which players may or may not be used against certain opposition.

In some athletics events, athletes and their coaches will know what tactics their opposition generally uses. The middle distance events are a good example of this. Some athletes with a strong sprint finish will wait until a certain point before outpacing the leading runners.

This might be at the final bend or perhaps with 150 metres to go. In racket games, to take another example, this might be shown in the formation that a doubles pair use or in certain shots they play.

It is in this area where information gathering might take the form of a **notational analysis.** You will not be expected to carry out a notational analysis for your examination, but it is a very useful **exercise** to help you to practise the skills necessary to become better at analysing performance.

Notation before a game

The practice of coaches scouting before a game is not new, and takes place in many sports. These coaches usually report what they have learned in written form and often with a lot of statistics. In invasion games this might include the number of shots by each individual player, how many were on target, how many missed the target and, if they were successful, where they shot from. There might also be

details on where individual players shoot from most often, the number of successful and unsuccessful passes made by each player, and over what distance. Information on certain set piece plays, such as free kicks in football, or short corners in hockey would also be noted. This information is then used for future games.

Notation during a game

This takes a similar form, but is for use during the game or at the interval. There are also ways to perform a notational analysis in racket and individual games and these are often shown after important tournaments – Wimbledon is a good example.

Key terms

- information gathering
- notational analysis
- scouts
- tactics
- teamwork

Player	Pos	Min	FGM–A	3PM–A	FTM–A	Off	Def	Tot	Ast	PF	ST	TO	BS	Pts
Tracey McGrady	F	31	13–22	2–6	4–7	5	1	6	5	2	2	1	1	36
Bo Outlaw	F	27	5–7	0–0	0–0	4	5	9	4	3	3	2	1	10
Andrew DeClercq	C	17	3–5	0–0	1–3	1	6	7	1	4	2	0	0	7
Mike Miller	G	32	5–14	1–5	0–0	3	2	5	3	3	1	2	0	11
Darrell Armstrong	G	26	1–6	0–3	2–3	1	4	5	6	1	0	3	0	4
Monty Williams		25	7–11	0–0	1–4	0	3	3	3	0	1	1	0	15
Troy Hudson		22	0–3	0–2	8–8	0	2	2	2	3	1	1	0	8
John Amaechi		18	5–7	0–0	6–10	1	2	3	1	2	0	2	1	16
Don Reid		17	2–4	0–0	2–2	3	5	8	1	5	0	3	1	6
Michael Doleac		17	1–5	0–0	0–0	0	3	3	0	3	2	0	0	2
Cory Alexander		8	1–3	1–3	0–2	0	1	1	1	2	2	0	0	5

Top titles mean:

Player	Position	Minutes played	FGM–A Field Goal Made-Attempted	3PM–A 3 point Made-Attempted	FTM–A Free Throw Made-Attempted
Rebounds-Offensive	Rebounds Defensive	Rebounds Total	Assists	Personal Fouls	Steals
Turn-overs	Blocked Shots	Total Points			

Source: Based on data from the nba.com website, © 2001 NBA Media Ventures

Notational analysis of Performance statistics based on Orlando Magic 120 Cleveland Cavaliers 94

13 What about the mental approach?

Your analysis of performance should include comments on team spirit. In very simple terms, you might note how certain players contribute to the activity even when they are not actually physically involved. This might take the form of encouraging and/or advising other players or a general contribution to the morale of the team.

14 Are there any star players?

In team games, there may be certain individual players who stand out. It may be necessary for the opposition to devise tactics to nullify these players or at least make it more difficult for them to play well. You should be able to pick out these players when you observe a performance and suggest ways to overcome them.

Task 10

Name a sport and an occasion when you watched a match in that sport. Name the star player. Explain to your partner why you thought that player was the star and how he or she influenced the game.

How does a good player influence the game?

There are a number of ways star players stand out. Some star players are easy to spot; others make contributions that are not so easy to see. Their star quality may be because certain factors that make their game easier for them – their natural assets or ability. For example, their **speed** may get them into positions quicker than other players – Michael Owen is an example. They may have great **power**, another important factor – Venus Williams, one of the world's leading tennis players, is an example of this. Players may also influence the game because their skills are very good in, for example, shooting in invasion games, serving or returning the service in racket games, or side-stepping an opponent in rugby.

Star players may have a great tactical knowledge of the game and would therefore play in a position where they could make best use of this.

Task 11

Name an invasion game and state a position from where a player could influence the game most.

Star players can inspire their team-mates

How do we know who is the best player?

There are two ways in which we can pick out the star players.

1   By observation – using subjective, **qualitative analysis**

Subjective means what we think, e.g. when we make a judgement based upon what we have seen or observed (watched carefully). Others may have a different opinion, so we need some ideas to argue our points. This is called qualitative analysis.

Task 12

Read the newspaper article below and analyse what the reporter has said. Is it opinion, or is it based on detailed information? Discuss this with your partner.

Anna Kournikova

2   By results – using objective, **quantitative analysis**

Objective means it is not opinion, but fact. We have results to prove it and these will back up, or not back up, our judgement of what we observed. This is called quantitative analysis.

Focus

So before we observe we must know:

- why we want to know (probably because we have been asked to do it!)
- what we want to observe – skills, game/competition, fitness
- how we are going to do it – qualitative and/or quantitative analysis
- when we are going to do it – in a practice session, during a game, in an examination.

Then we must make sure we are getting good information!

Key terms

- **mental approach**
- **qualitative analysis**
- **quantitative analysis**
- **star players**
- **tactical knowledge**
- **team spirit**

147 doubles

They used to say in tennis circles that the lovely, delectable Anna Kournikova didn't have a fault. Then came a glitch in her serve.

From Wimbledon champions to humble qualifiers they gathered, huddled around TV sets in the players' area to watch the latest phenomenon in tennis.

Yet this was no newly-arrived prodigy parading her talents and capturing the attention of Australian Open protagonists.

This was the box-office performance of Anna Kournikova and her incredible disappearing serve.

Tennis has never seen a case of the yips on such a grand scale. The 17-year-old Russian served a staggering 31 double faults while limping across the line into the third round with a 1–6, 6–4, 10–8 victory over Miho Saeki.

Embarrassingly, she totals 147 double faults in a seven-match spell dating back to November last year.

After leading 5–0 in the deciding set, she had to serve for the match eight times before overcoming the unheralded Japanese girl.

Strangely, the remainder of Kournikova's impressive all-court game has survived this ongoing disaster, and when she managed to deliver the ball into play, she was good enough to overcome gifting the equivalent of nearly eight games of free points to her shocked opponent.

Not surprisingly, the root of the problem appears to be psychological, not in any glaring technical weakness, although she is tossing the ball unusually high.

Despite this, she has been spotted on the practice court with all manner of tinkering mechanics. The wisdom of such a policy has to be questioned.

Source: *Daily Mail*, 22 January 1999

Analysis (examining in detail)

When making an analysis, the idea is to know what is actually happening and why. There are several qualities we need to have to make a good job of analysis and coaching. The analysis of performance criteria will help us to find out what some of these qualities are.

- You need to know the rules of the game or activity you are going to analyse and the competition rules, if relevant. Many activities have terminology of their own; words and phrases that only mean something to people involved with the sport.
- You will need to know how to observe. Although the skill of analysis might seem obvious, you should know a variety of ways to analyse performance.
- Once you have analysed a performance, it must be evaluated. To do this, you must recognize both its weaknesses *and* its strengths. To evaluate a performance well, you must know how the performance should look at its very best and compare what you saw with the perfect model.
- When you have the information you want and have evaluated it, you must be able to plan how to use it to improve:
  - future performances by planning suitable practices and/or
  - to improve fitness through training. You should reflect back on your PEP to help you to do this.

- You must show an understanding of the roles of leadership such as captaincy, or be able to coach in your particular sport. This also takes us back into the rules that are an important aspect of leadership skills. Coaches need to know the rules of the game and of competitions, so that they can plan strategies and tactics to improve performance.

The quality of the analysis depends on several factors. The first of these is the quality of the observation, so some preparation and/or practice needs to be done first.

In the initial stages, choose something simple to analyse – something you are good at. Write down the different aspects of the skill first like those in the table below, then watch carefully as your partner performs. Put a plus or a cross next to the different aspects of the skill to show if you are happy with it or not, then you can check it later. Practice like this will also help you to know the perfect model (how it should be done) in some detail.

From our observations, we can analyse the performance. This shows that we are satisfied in a number of areas, but not in others and we have made a note of these. With experience, you may not need to write down the information, but will be able to carry out this sort of analysis visually, or subjectively (qualitatively).

Skill: basketball lay-up shot

Aspect of skill	Un/successful	Problem	Work on
Dribble	X	Head down	Head up dribble
Pick-up	+		
1–2 count	+		
Jump	+		
Release	X	Hand position	Demonstrate
Aim	X	Sighting	Look up to backboard
Force	+		
Landing	+		
Result	X	20%	Check %

Key terms

- observe
- the perfect model
- qualitative
- quantitative

Evaluation (assessing)

Now that we have done the analysis, we must **evaluate** (assess) the quality of the performance/skill/tactics/fitness factors.

In order for you to evaluate the quality, you must know what the performance should look like (the perfect model). For students, this knowledge may come from playing/competing in the activity, being coached in the activity, or being taught by the teacher. It may also come from photographs, demonstrations by good players, posters, or videos.

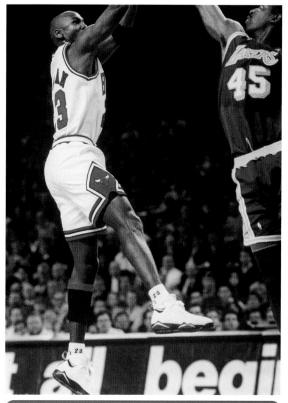

2 What are the strengths shown in this picture?

From our analysis on the opposite page, we have assessed the lay-up shot and decided that there are four problem areas. So we now know what to work on:

- the dribble
- the release
- the aim
- and we must check the result.

How we work on them, and the order in which we work on them, now has to be decided.

1 What is the most obvious weakness shown in this picture?

Task

Evaluate the two pictures on this page. What is the most obvious weakness shown in picture 1? What are the strengths shown in picture 2? (Find at least four.)

Key terms

- **assess**
- **evaluate**
- **the perfect model**
- **result**

Planning (working out the details)

In planning we must work out ways to get the performer to perform better.

This will depend on what needs to be improved. In the basketball example (page 22), it is a skill, the lay-up shot, that needs to be improved.

Skills may be improved through practices or drills, which can be learned from the teacher, from a book, from posters or devised by the student. However, a difficult skill or a new skill may have to be broken down and learned piece by piece and then put back together to form the whole skill again. The lay-up shot is a good example of this.

Setting priorities

In the example of the lay-up shot, where there is more than one problem, we must decide our priorities. Which is the most important fault to correct? Which is the second and which the third? We may decide that in improving one point, another will automatically improve. So we might decide on the following course of action.

Start with the release

1 Start with the release.

2 Demonstrate the hand position for the release.

3 Stand near the basket, at the correct angle, take aim and then release correctly.

4 Practise dribbling without shooting but with head up, watching the coach.

Practise dribbling with head up

5 Practise the lay-up shot.

6 Ask yourself: 'Has the performance of the skill improved?'

Tasks

a Choose a sport. Take a skill in this sport and name three faults that might occur with this skill. Write them out in order of importance and then devise a method of improving the skills similar to the way set out on this page.

b In the activity you are practising at present, state how you will set about improving your performance in the skills required.

Player	Points scored	Shots missed	Total points	Total misses
4	2	x	2	1
5	2	x.x.x.x.x.x.x	2	7
6	0	x.x	0	2
7	2.3	x.x.x.x	5	4
8	2.2.2	x.x	6	2
9	2.2.3.2.3.3.2.2	x.x	19	2
10	3.2	x.x.x	5	3
11	2	x.x.x.x.x.x.x	2	7

Basketball analysis

A basketball notational analysis (see page 19) might look like the table above.

What will an evaluation of this analysis show?

- Number 9 scores a lot.
- Numbers 4, 5, 6 and 11 scored only six points between them.
- Numbers 5 and 11 missed a lot.
- Number 4 actually scored 50%.
- Number 10 scored 40%.
- Number 7 scored 30%.
- Number 8 scored 60%.
- Number 9 scored 80%.

Information it would be useful to know

It would help to know if this analysis was of *them* or *us* as this will affect our interpretation of the information.

It would help to know something about the tactics that were used.

1 What defensive system was used by each team, and what attacking formations?

2 It would help to know where the shots were taken from; were they close to the basket or shot from further out?

More detail might show us:

1 What type of shot was missed?

2 Did we miss lay-up shots or jump shots from long range?

3 What positions did each individual player score from?

What might we plan from this evaluation?

- Number 9 scores a lot. If s/he is on our side give her/him the ball!
- If s/he is not on our side we need to take some form of action to stop him/her!
- If s/he is not on our side, who was marking her/him?
- Numbers 5, 7 and 11 need to practise shooting and until they can shoot well they should not take too many shots in the game.
- Why did number 4 only have two shots?

We might learn from this evaluation that in the next game we will find:

- special ways to get the ball to number 9 more often (or ways to stop number 9 next time we play this team)
- ways to make better use of number 4.

In practice sessions there will be:

- extra shooting practice for numbers 5, 7 and 11.

Key terms

- evaluation
- planning
- priorities

Swimming analysis

100 m freestyle				
Lengths (25 m pool)	1	2	3	4
Time for each length	15.2	15.5	15.5	16.1
Accumulative time in seconds	15.2	30.7	46.2	62.3
Accumulative distance	25 m	50 m	75 m	100 m

A swimming notational analysis on fitness/time/performance might look like the table above.

What will an evaluation of this analysis show?

- The first length was the fastest.
- The fourth length was the slowest.
- The second and third lengths were the same.
- The second and third lengths were slower than the first but faster than the last.

Information it would be useful to know

It would help to know:

- the swimmer's personal best time
- their final position in the race
- their position at the end of each length.

Analysing during a competition is a good way to identify training needs

What might the swimmer and coach plan from this evaluation?

The training programme for the swimmer might be changed in order to improve their stamina, so that they will perform better in the final length in future races. The new programme might be planned for a six-week period, or up to the next race. Then a similar analysis might be taken and used to compare with the previous analysis.

Physical fitness can also be tested on such things as:

- work-rate
- speed
- strength
- **heart rate** (see page 68)
- **recovery rate** (see page 76).

They may decide that they will include some strength training and land conditioning. Land conditioning is training that takes place without using swimming – it could be running or circuit training, for example. These are covered later in the book (pages 94–7).

The swimmer might also change the tactics for the next race and not swim quite so fast on the first length, trying to save a little of their strength for the final length, thereby making the pace more evenly distributed over the four lengths.

We must remember that this is an analysis of the facts. The coach might have observed some errors in the swimmer's technique which could be improved to help to produce a better performance. So the two methods can work together.

Key terms

- evaluation
- personal best
- technique

Feedback – using what you have learned

The temperament of players and performers may be very different. Some may respond to being shouted at, while others need lots of encouragement and quietly being told what they did wrong and how to improve.

> ## Task
>
> Think of an occasion when someone fed back to you or to a team-mate and really got them to improve, or got the best out of them. Either write a very short account of this or explain it to a partner.

Giving information about the performance

Getting information is one thing – giving it to the performer for the best possible outcome is another. Some coaches are very good at analysing both individual and team performance, but cannot always get the information across to their players or team, so that they clearly understand what is required of them. Feeding back the information is a great skill which coaches have to work on to get the best results. Different approaches are needed for different players or different occasions.

What to feed back on

When coaching during a competition or game situation, there may be several things to feed back on all at the same time. The coach may have to be selective in what information they actually need to get across first. It may depend on what type of activity it is. A gymnastic competition is a quiet affair compared to a rugby match. To a gymnast, the **feedback** is more likely to be on the skills than on tactics, but a half-time team talk in rugby is almost certain to include tactics.

Feedback after a game might include comments on the players' fitness, effort, emotions, or temperament. Some coaches feed back on too much and the players may find it difficult to absorb it all at once, especially in the heat of competition. Feedback also depends on whether it is to an individual, a pair, a whole team, or to one member.

When is it best to feed back?

Once again this will depend on the activity. In many situations, feedback may be immediate, for example, during a game, but most coaches will also give some general feedback when the activity has finished. What and how they feed back at this time may well depend on the result!

During a training session, feedback is generally continuous, especially if it is a skill session designed to improve a specific aspect of the sport. Coaches will also feed back on the last match, then again just before a competition.

How can we feed back? And how often?

As well as feeding back verbally, visually and by demonstrations, good coaches often involve performers by asking for their opinions and ideas. Good performers know whether they have done well or not. Some coaches feed back more than others, but novice coaches usually need to see more than one attempt before making comments.

Remember, feedback must be designed to get the best out of the player and to improve performance.

Key term

- feedback

Analysing performance and using feedback in the examination

In most coaching situations, you would expect to feed back to the performer, player and/or team, but in your PE examination you will be expected to feed back to your teacher and/or the moderator and possibly also to the performer or team you have been analysing. Remember also that feedback can be positive or negative. Positive feedback could be comments such as 'You're doing well', 'That was good', 'Keep up the good work'. Negative feedback could be comments like 'You keep losing the ball', 'You've missed so many chances'. Feedback should be constructive, for example, 'They have some big central defenders, so we need to keep the ball on the floor and use the speed of our faster strikers'.

The teacher or moderator may ask what is known as an 'open' question. This will be a question that will need more than just a yes or no answer. For example: 'Tell me what you know about the rules concerning moving with the ball in basketball.' A question on tactics would enable you to develop an opinion – again not just a yes or no answer.

Demonstrating feedback

You may be given the opportunity to teach or coach other students or a team and this will allow you to feed back as a coach might do and demonstrate your knowledge in this way. So it is important to note the points illustrated and to know and practise feedback in a variety of situations.

The table below illustrates:
● what could be analysed in some sports
● how it could be analysed
● what method of feedback could be used.

'I've followed your suggestions, simplified my grip, adjusted my stance and the ball is heading for the hole...'

Sport	Analyse	How to analyse	Feedback
Football	Shots on target	Notational	Verbal/visual
Golf	Swing	Video	Verbal/visual
Netball	Shooting	Visual	Verbal

Planning feedback

Remember the areas in the analysis of performance criteria and try to build your feedback around these. Include details of fitness and training programmes for your particular activity and especially your knowledge of the perfect model.

Your knowledge of fitness training should come from your own experience and evidence from your PEP and from using knowledge gained in theory lessons.

If you are analysing a skill, you can demonstrate your ability to improve players' skills by setting up a skill practice, perhaps breaking down the skill and then suggesting ways to improve before building it back up again into the full skill situation.

Some activities actually lend themselves to notational analysis and a knowledge of this could help you on the day. For example, you could explain how you could record successful/ unsuccessful shooting in an invasion game.

It is essential for you to practise the analysis of performance, especially feeding back verbally. This can be done on many occasions during practical lessons by helping other students. It is also helpful to have a knowledge of your own performance and to know your own strengths and weaknesses so that you can also answer questions on that. In team games, you can demonstrate your ability by knowing how well the team is performing, the tactics, why the team is winning or losing, how the tactics might be changed and what might result from this change of tactics.

Key terms

- **rules**
- **skill practice**
- **strengths and weaknesses**
- **tactics**
- **verbal feedback**
- **visual feedback**

A knowledge of practices will help you in your analysis of performance

Reasons for taking part in physical activity

Exercise and physical activity help people to tone their muscles and increase their strength. This in turn:

improves body shape

and ...

helps the individual to look and feel good

about themselves and more easily meet the normal demands of life. It also ...

contributes to good health

often enabling us to cope better with sickness and disease. Despite what some people think it ...

Allowing for physical challenge

Stimulates competition

can be enjoyable!

Some people take part because it ...

can help to relieve stress and tension

by acting as a distraction from problems, concentrating the mind and ...

allowing for physical challenge

which is very satisfying. The opportunity to work in teams and groups helps to ...

improve co-operation

and it also ...

Allows us to take part in sport

Activities are stimulating

stimulates competition

Physical activity also …

gives opportunities for aesthetic appreciation

which means enjoying the beauty that comes from certain activities. Sport and physical activities also …

encourage social mixing

and meeting other people as team-mates, opponents, or other club members. This often …

encourages friendships

whilst it also …

allows us to take part in sport

Many people find that the …

activities are stimulating

and through these activities many people …

gain membership of sports clubs

Task 1

In your exercise books, draw three boxes with the titles:

- Personal or physical
- Psychological
- Social.

Then put each of the reasons given here for taking part in physical activity into the appropriate box.

Key terms

- **aesthetic appreciation**
- **body shape**
- **co-operation**
- **good health**
- **stress and tension**

Why do people take part in physical activity?

Sport presents a very wide and varied array of opportunities. Most people who take part in sport are amateurs who pay for the pleasure of taking part. Those who are paid to take part, coach or instruct are the lucky few who get paid for doing what they enjoy.

This section looks into the reasons why the vast majority of people take part in sport, fitness and exercise. They do so in one of three ways: they can either play, or they can train/exercise or they can do a combination of both by training and playing, or training to play. Their reasons for taking part may be very different.

Sport is enjoyed by people from all age groups

1 To improve body shape

Training and taking part in sport can improve body shape, and a programme of planned, well-thought-out exercises, weight training and playing sport can do this (see pages 94–7). The muscles are strengthened and made more flexible, and in doing so they become less flabby and more toned. In expending energy while exercising and playing we use up excess calories, which can contribute to a controlled weight-loss programme. Many people take part in physical activity to improve their body shape. However, this is best done together with a controlled **diet** (see page 42).

2 To look and feel better

The second reason follows on quite naturally from the first one, because if you take part in sport and exercise regularly, as your body shape improves you will begin to look better and feel better about yourself.

3 For good health

People who exercise usually cope better if they become ill. This is true for common colds and flu, but also, and much more importantly, for serious illnesses as well. Our ability to withstand and recover from serious illness or operations is related to how fit we are, and especially how our heart and lung functions improve with exercise (see page 62).

4 For enjoyment

The reason for taking part in sport may affect our enjoyment of it. If we are made to do it, we may not want to do it. However, some people take part for no other reason than they like it, so it *can* be enjoyable. Observe the players at your local sports centre or tennis courts – they may be intense but they are probably there because they choose to be.

Task 2

For each of reasons 1–4 on this page, try to think of one example of each which you could use to illustrate the point. The photograph shows one example – enjoyment!

5 To relieve stress and tension

Taking part in sport can sometimes be stressful. Imagine getting on your starting blocks for the 100 metres final in the Olympic Games, or walking out to the Centre Court for your first Wimbledon final! However, taking part can form a distraction from the turmoil of daily life, and can relieve stress and tension from work and family pressures. While those problems may not go away, at least taking part will get you away from them temporarily, and may sometimes make it easier to face them when you have finished your activity.

6 For a physical challenge

Starting back to sport after a long lay-off, perhaps as an adult who has not taken part since leaving school, or coming back from injury, or taking on a seemingly impossible task (e.g. running the London Marathon), allows for a physical challenge which can be very satisfying. Running a marathon is a good example because the physical challenge is often the most striking memory for those who take part for the fun of it.

7 & 8 For co-operation and competition

Many sports are played in teams and working in groups helps to improve co-operation – teamwork – which we often need in our everyday lives. As well as co-operation it also stimulates competition, as does a Sunday league football match, or an inter-club table tennis match.

9 For the aesthetic qualities

Beauty in a performance may not be appreciated as much as winning, and some sports may lend themselves more to this – for example, ice dance. But many supporters of games like rugby and football would still appreciate the **aesthetic qualities** of a great try at Twickenham or goal at Wembley.

10 To mix socially

Some people may choose to run or train on their own, but most sports give a lot of opportunity to mix socially, both with your own team members and the opposition. Many friendships may come about, or last, because of a sporting connection.

Sport provides opportunities to make friends

Opportunities to take part in sport

Sports centres are very popular and are often run by the local council to provide various opportunities, not only for children, but for children, parents and grandparents alike.

Task 3

Write down a list of as many activities as you can which are provided for at your local sports centre. Include both sporting and training opportunities.

Joining a club

Some sports and activities can take place without joining a sports or fitness club, but gaining membership of a club often opens up a range of opportunities for further activity. For example, when someone first joins a club they may not intend to take part competitively, but as they improve and get to know other members they may want to try their sport competitively – first within their club and then perhaps to represent their club in open competition.

Task 4

Write down all the reasons (1–10) shown on these two pages. Against each, write the name of a sport or training activity that has enabled you to achieve or satisfy the reason for taking part. For example:

For enjoyment – cross country running

Key terms

- **aesthetic qualities**
- **body shape**
- **good health**
- **physical challenge**
- **stimulate competition**
- **stress and tension**

Factors affecting participation and performance

On Friday 22 September 2000, millions in Britain stayed up late to watch the British coxless four gain victory by just 0.38 seconds over Italy, their enthusiasm generated by the now legendary Sir Steven Redgrave, who gained his fifth gold medal in the team's victory. His story includes a catalogue of factors that affect participation and in particular factors that affect performance.

At 13, Steven and some other boys were invited by their teacher to try rowing at the local club. Steven showed potential and he enjoyed this first experience, as did his best friend. Three of the many factors that affect participation in sport are enjoyment, social mixing (encouraging friendships) and ability. No doubt many of the other factors on the last four pages contributed to him continuing to participate in the sport.

Champions in sport come in many shapes and sizes, from tiny gymnasts to heavyweight contestants. Body build is an obvious factor that affects performance. This was one of the factors that gave Steven an advantage over other rowers. He is 1 m 96 cm (6 ft 5 in) tall, 105 kg (16 st 7 lb) and has long arms that increase the leverage he can apply to the oar when rowing.

Training over a long period of time has helped Steven to develop other factors affecting his performance. He has a big strong heart to pump blood, and therefore oxygen, around his body, with a resting pulse rate of between 40 and 45 beats per minute (b.p.m.). The average person's pulse rate is around 72 b.p.m. During the Olympic final, his pulse rate was probably somewhere around 180–200 b.p.m. He also has a huge lung capacity with a VO_2 max of 7. The average is 4 to 5. His muscle to fat ratio is around 7, whereas the average for men is 15–20. To maintain his energy stores and muscle, he takes in 6000 calories a day – that is 4000 more than the average male!

While positive factors can improve performance, negative factors can reduce performance. Many great champions overcome such difficulties. Steven is a diabetic and also suffers from a very debilitating condition called ulcerative colitis – a severe bowel condition.

Sir Steve Redgrave and his gold medal from the Sydney 2000 Olympics

Task 1

a   Copy the five headings on page 35 and put down as many factors as possible under each one that you think would affect a potential sports champion.

   Note – not all sports need the same factors (e.g. a basketball player needs very different ones from a champion jockey).

b   Bring a photograph of a sporting champion to the next lesson (newspapers are a good source). Be prepared to describe what factors makes this person a champion. You may be able to think of some other factors than the ones listed here.

When he won his first gold medal in Los Angeles in 1984, Steven was just 22. Being young is an advantage in many sports. In Sydney 2000, he was 38, which was considered a distinct disadvantage! However, he did have the advantage of being more experienced.

These and many other factors that affect performance will be explained as you work through this book. You will be given the chance to see how you measure up to many of them. During your course, you must learn to understand the various factors that affect performance, both in a positive sense and in a negative sense. You must be able to relate them to yourself and your sport, and also to recognize factors that affect other people in their activities.

Factors that make a champion

There are a number of different factors that make a champion and they fall into different categories.

1 Psychological factors

Determination might be one of the factors under this heading. Many of the great champions have shown this in their efforts to reach the top in their sport, and it is something that most champions have, whatever their sporting area.

2 Sociological factors

Under this heading we might have such factors as a supportive home environment. Many champions say that their parents have spent many hours taking them to training sessions and collecting them afterwards. Parents of swimmers are famous for this!

3 Luck

There have been many champions who have said that it was a stroke of luck that helped them to become a champion. Muhammad Ali had his bicycle stolen and because of that he met the man who started him boxing. Perhaps he would not have done so had things worked out differently that day. So being in the right place at the right time was lucky for him.

4 Motor skills

Having good **motor skills** is very important – that innate talent which helps to give a person a head start on the rest of us. If one particular motor skill could be singled out it might well be speed. This is a factor that is necessary for many sports.

5 Health and fitness

If you are not lucky enough to have a good body build or **body composition** for your sport, then the chances of reaching the top are reduced. However it is possible, as you will see, to improve in this area, as it is in some others too.

Key terms

- determination
- health and fitness
- motor skills
- psychological factors
- sociological factors
- supportive home environment
- the right place at the right time

If Muhammad Ali's bike hadn't been stolen, he might never have become a champion!

Other factors

There are many other factors that help people become champions. Some champions may have more or different abilities than others and it may depend upon the sport in which they take part. Frankie Dettorie is a great jockey who has ridden many winning horses. He is small in stature and light in weight, factors that certainly suit him for his sport, but might not for others.

The will to win

The will to win is another important factor. This might be described as a willingness to continue trying to reach the top in the sport of your choice. This, of course, will not get you there if you do not have some other factors in your favour. Many young people will overcome some of their shortcomings to reach the top, but they probably have some other factors in their favour. As the great decathlete Daley Thompson once said, 'There is more than one way to the top of the mountain'.

Parents

Parents can have an influence on their children's choice of sport and how good they become at it. For example, Tim Henman, Martina Hinges and the Williams sisters all had parents who strongly encouraged their tennis playing and supported them in this sport. Tiger Woods is another example of someone who was encouraged to play his sport from a very early age. However, other sporting champions got to the top without any kind of help from their parents.

Co-ordination

If you do not have good **co-ordination** in tennis, golf or other such games, you will not be able to hit the ball, certainly not well enough to become a champion. This is another factor needed to reach the top.

Muscular strength

Another area in which you can improve is **muscular strength.** However, there are some aspects of strength that some people are naturally better off in to start with. Of course, there are sports in which strength is a crucial factor affecting performance.

The school you go to

The school you go to may actually pre-determine the sport that you take up. As we saw in the case of Steven Redgrave (p. 34), a teacher can have a big influence on encouraging participation in a sport. If you go to a public school, statistics show that your chances of being exposed to playing cricket are better. Many children actually choose their secondary school based upon the sports in which a particular school excels.

Public schools often have good facilities for cricket

Flexibility

Flexibility is important in most sports but more so in some than in others. We are all more flexible as young children than as adults unless we work at it, but natural flexibility will help.

Good friends

Friends can have a big influence on some people and it is sometimes not easy to go off to training when your friends are going off somewhere else. However, in order to reach the top, the influence or support that young sportspeople get from their friends may be very important.

Key terms

- co-ordination
- flexibility
- muscular strength
- will to win

Task 2

a Draw up a table using the five categories on page 35 as the table headings. Then take the factors which have been discussed on pages 36 and 37 plus those shown on the factors affecting performance tree below and fit each one under what you think is the correct heading. Use your answer to task **a** on page 34 to help you.

b Build up a picture of the factors that go to make a sporting champion. If you think you have some others to add, then do so.

For the purposes of your GCSE course, the two most important areas to look at in detail are motor skills and the one we will investigate next – health and fitness.

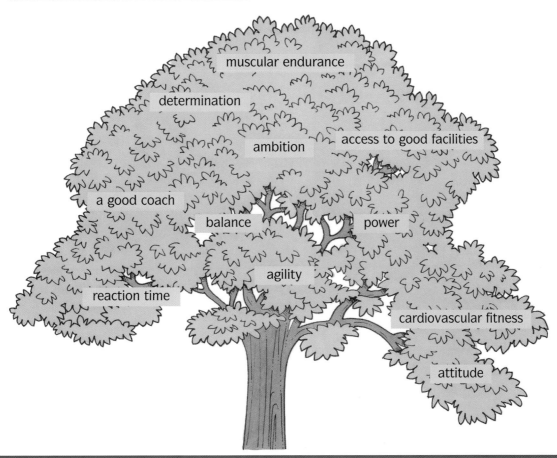

muscular endurance

determination

ambition

access to good facilities

a good coach

balance

power

agility

reaction time

cardiovascular fitness

attitude

The 'Factors affecting performance' tree

Health related exercise

Health

Over the last 100 years in the western world, **infectious** diseases (those which are passed on from one person to another) have declined dramatically, but **health** problems brought about by lack of exercise have increased. Charles Corbin (an American health expert) refers to these as 'hypokinetic diseases', which he says are due to lack of activity. This can be accounted for, to some extent, by the change from jobs needing physical effort, such as farming, to jobs that are mostly done sitting down (sedentary jobs), such as office jobs.

Immunization (also called vaccination or inoculation) has helped to reduce the spread of infectious disease

There are a number of reasons why infectious diseases have been brought more under control. Improved **hygiene** and general cleanliness are among the reasons. For example, hospitals are now much cleaner places than they were 100 years ago.

Tasks

a What other reasons can you think of which have helped to reduce deaths due to infectious disease?

b In your exercise books, list three infectious diseases.

c It is said that prevention is better than cure. Explain how you think we can prevent hypokinetic diseases.

d Name one hypokinetic disease and say how you think it might be treated.

Definitions

When you have to write a definition, it may help to think of it as explaining the meaning of a word to a younger brother or sister.

health	a state of complete mental, physical and social well-being, not simply the absence of disease or infirmity
exercise	a form of physical activity done primarily to improve one's health and physical fitness

Source: Edexcel specification

Fitness and performance

Many more people are now aware and concerned about their own health and this has brought about a change of attitude to exercise. It is not just the sporting elite who enjoy and seek fitness. Ordinary people also want the benefits that go with fitness and some go to extraordinary lengths to achieve high levels of **performance**. The London Marathon is a good example of this.

fitness	the ability to meet the demands of the environment
performance	how well a task is completed

Source: Edexcel specification

Health related exercise (HRE)

Exercise is a **physical activity** that improves health and physical fitness. It is thought to improve mental health and relieve stress. Exercising together also helps people to socialize. (See participation factors on pages 30–3.)

There are five main areas of fitness that together help us to be physically healthy: cardiovascular fitness, muscular strength, muscular endurance, flexibility and body composition. The combination of these areas is known as **health related exercise** (HRE). In itself, HRE does not guarantee good health as 'a state of complete mental, physical and social well being' (see the definition on page 38). The example of Steven Redgrave (page 34) shows this well. Although he is physically in peak condition, he has two serious health problems – diabetes and ulcerative colitis. However, his extreme fitness has helped him to live a physically very active life.

The five areas of HRE

Cardiovascular fitness
Cardiovascular fitness is concerned with the healthy working of the heart, blood and blood vessels. It is the most important aspect of HRE because it helps us to lead an active lifestyle and to continue to take part in physically active sports as we get older.

Muscular strength
Muscular strength enables us to lift heavy weights – important if we do a job or take part in sports that involve exerting great force.

Muscular endurance
Muscular endurance is concerned with lifting lighter weights repeatedly without getting unduly tired. Both of these aspects of HRE are covered on pages 100–105.

Flexibility
This area of HRE enables us to have a good range of movement in our joints. Stretching to touch our toes would be an example of flexibility. If we do not work at it, we lose it!

Body composition
Body composition is the percentage of body weight which is fat, muscle and bone. We can influence our body composition through exercise and diet, but it is largely down to genes. Body build, as in Steven Redgrave's case, is an important factor in sport, but body composition is also very important too.

You will investigate all five areas of HRE in more detail as you go through the course. You will look at how to improve performance in each area and how each is important to a healthy lifestyle – all information you need to know to do well in your GCSE. We will start with body composition, together with the important factors of diet – body weight and body build.

Key terms

- body composition
- cardiovasular fitness
- exercise
- flexibility
- fitness
- health
- health related exercise (HRE)
- infectious
- muscular endurance
- muscular strength
- performance
- physical activity

Body composition

As we have seen from the work so far, body composition is important to both the top sportspeople and to ordinary people. The elite athletes have a good body build for their sport and one reason for taking part in sport is that it improves body shape. Body composition is one of the five aspects of health and fitness – or HRE, to use the proper term – and it is important to know about for your GCSE course. So what does it involve?

We can begin by looking at how specialists and experts in this area define, describe and explain certain points. It will help you if you can remember either how they do it, or show that you can do it using your own words. Where possible, try to use the correct terms or phrases. Also remember these three words:

● define

● describe

● explain.

Examination questions may ask you to deal with a question in one of these three ways. For example: 'Define the word fitness.'

What is body composition?

Body composition, as described by Neil Armstrong of the PEA Research Centre at Exeter University, is:

'the relative make-up of the body in muscle, fat, bone and other vital parts.'

Another definition, from the Edexcel specification, is:

'the percentage of body weight which is fat, muscle and bone.'

Body weight can be assessed as two separate factors:

1 **Body fat** or percentage body fat, which weighing ourselves on scales tells us nothing about.

2 **Lean body mass**, *'the mass of bones, muscles, connective tissue and organs'*,

as defined by Davis, Kimmet and Auty (*Physical Education Theory and Practice*).

It is possible to measure percentage body fat and then work out your lean body mass. You may have the chance to do this experiment later as well as experiments to find your ideal body weight.

The first thing that will spring to mind for most people when they think about body composition is their weight. It is likely that you are at a difficult age to measure height against weight because you are growing rapidly. Frame size is also very important. There are numerous height-to-weight tables for adults and insurance companies often use them when people take out life insurance. It is a delicate subject to study, but for those who wish to experiment you could try the following tasks.

Tasks

a ● Measure your wrist girth around the part of your wrist where your watch would normally be. Using chart A on the opposite page, work out your frame size: small, medium or large.

   ● Now use chart B or C to work out what your desirable weight should be. Remember there are different charts for men and women because desirable weights will be different.

b Now work out your weight according to chart D. This time men and women are measured from the same chart.

c Compare the two results, as charts A–C are American while chart D is British.

Remember, all these charts are for adults and this is only an experiment. However, if your parents or other adults want to use the charts, chart D is issued by the Health Education Authority and is based on figures that were produced in the UK and are used frequently.

Chart A – Determining frame size using wrist size in inches

Frame	Men	Women
small	6 inches or less	5.5 or less
medium	6.25 – 7.25	5.75
large	7.5 or more	6 or more

Chart B – Desirable body weight for women (kgs)

Height (metres)	Small frame	Medium frame	Large frame
1·47	46–50	49–55	53–59
1·49	47–51	50–56	54–61
1·52	47–52	51–57	55–62
1·54	48–53	52–58	56–63
1·57	49–55	53–60	58–65
1·60	50–56	54–61	59–67
1·62	51–57	56–62	61–68
1·65	53–59	58–64	62–70
1·67	54–60	59–65	63–72
1·70	55–61	60–67	65–74
1·72	56–62	61–68	66–76
1·75	58–64	63–69	68–77
1·77	59–65	64–71	69–78
1·80	60–67	65–72	70–80
1·82	62–68	67–73	71–81

Chart C – Desirable body weight for men (kgs)

Height (metres)	Small frame	Medium frame	Large frame
1·57	58–60	59–64	62–68
1·60	59–61	60–65	63–69
1·62	59–62	61–66	64–70
1·65	60–63	62–67	65–72
1·67	61–64	63–68	66–74
1·70	62–66	64–70	67–76
1·72	63–67	65–71	69–78
1·75	64–68	67–72	70–80
1·77	65–70	68–74	71–82
1·80	66–71	70–75	73–83
1·82	67–73	71–77	74–85
1·85	70–74	72–79	76–87
1·87	71–76	74–81	78–89
1·90	71–78	76–82	80–92
1·93	73–80	77–85	82–93

Chart D – Height-to-weight chart for men and women

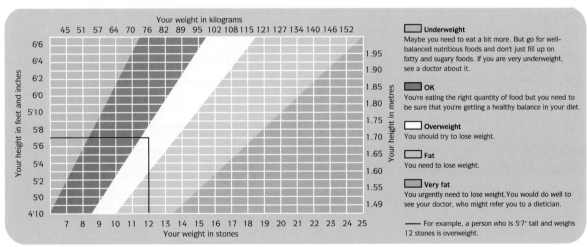

Source: Health Development Agency

Body composition and your PE course

Many of the points involved with body composition are important aspects of your GCSE course, so in the following units we will look at these in some detail.

Key terms

- body composition
- body fat
- body shape
- define, describe and explain
- health-related exercise
- lean body mass

Diet

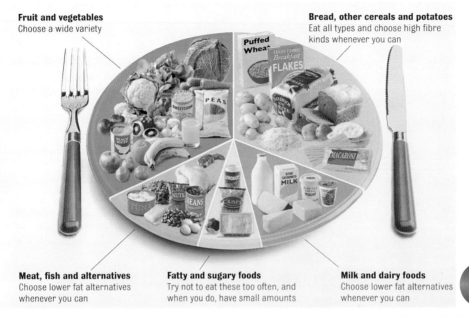

Fruit and vegetables
Choose a wide variety

Bread, other cereals and potatoes
Eat all types and choose high fibre kinds whenever you can

Meat, fish and alternatives
Choose lower fat alternatives whenever you can

Fatty and sugary foods
Try not to eat these too often, and when you do, have small amounts

Milk and dairy foods
Choose lower fat alternatives whenever you can

The Balance of Good Health

Source: Health Development Agency

Diet is one of those words that is sometimes misused. Diet can be defined as 'the normal food we eat', but there are also special diets, for example, to lose weight or gain weight, diets because of moral values (e.g. a vegetarian diet) or because of food allergies, such as wheat flour intolerance.

Weight loss can be brought about in one of three ways, but each is concerned with **energy balance.** We need energy to produce muscle contractions, and for the growth and repair of tissues (see pages 47 and 66).

Joules and calories

Energy can be measured using joules or calories, but these are defined differently.

- A joule is defined as the energy needed when 1 kilogram (kg) is moved 1 metre by a force of 1 newton (N).
- A calorie (cal) is defined as the energy needed to raise the temperature of 1 gram of water by 1 degree (from 14.5° to 15.5° C).

When large units are involved, such as they are in diets, the terms kilojoule (kJ) (which equals 1000 joules) or megajoule (MJ) (1 million joules) are used. When, as an alternative, the term calorie is used, the kilocalorie (kcal) (which equals 1000 calories) is generally used.

Energy balance

Energy balance means taking in (eating) and using up (through work, exercise, etc.) an equal number of calories or kilocalories. We all have our own metabolism or rate of using up energy – known as our **metabolic rate.** This is why some people may eat less food but actually put on weight, while others appear to be able to eat anything without putting on a pound.

- Males between the age of 15 and 18 need about 11.51 MJ (2755 kcal) per day.
- Females between the age of 15 and 18 need about 8.83 MJ (2100 kcal) per day.

Losing weight

People who want to lose weight usually do so by using one of three possible methods.

1 Decreasing kilocalorie energy intake.
2 Increasing kilocalorie energy expenditure.
3 Using a combination of both.

Most people would agree that the third method is the best, giving best results and being the most long lasting.

It should be remembered that dieting to lose weight should be carried out under the guidance of an expert such as your GP or a state registered dietician. Remember, dieting to excess can be very dangerous.

Overweight, overfat, obese

These words do not mean the same thing. Charles Corbin, an American expert on health-related exercise, defines them as:

overweight	having weight in excess of normal. Not harmful unless it is accompanied by overfatness
overfat	having too much body composition as fat; men, having more than 19% of total body composition as fat; for women 26%
obese or obesity	extreme overweight, often considered as 20% to 35% above 'normal'; probably best described as an extreme overfat condition

Obesity in the UK

In the UK we use only two terms, overweight and obese, and research has shown that problems with adults who are overweight and obese have increased in the UK in recent years.

These conditions carry with them certain health risks such as the risk of cancer and coronary heart disease (CHD) – including heart attacks and strokes, as well as high blood pressure.

Studies have shown that, if anything, the problem with children is even worse and it is suggested that it is just as likely to be through lack of exercise as through eating too much.

Factors affecting an individual's diet

Each individual sportsperson's diet will depend upon a number of factors. Their natural body build (see pages 52–3), their particular sport, or even the position they play in their particular sport, can all have an influence on their diet.

For example, in rugby a player's weight might reflect the position they play – the short stocky hooker, the big strong prop forward or, by comparison, the more slightly built scrum half. In football and hockey, goalkeepers may use less energy in a game than midfield players, in the same way that people who play sport and exercise need a different diet from those who do not exercise.

Task

Write down and compare two other sports or events, such as athletics, in which you can find people who need more or less energy than others, or who may be quite different in weight from other participants.

Key terms

- diet
- energy balance
- kilocalories and kilojoules
- natural body build
- obese
- overweight

The effects of under/overeating on body weight and performance

What is meant by optimum body weight?

optimum	'most favourable' or 'best compromise'
	Oxford English Dictionary

Most sportspeople get to know the weight at which they perform best and make an effort to keep within certain limits of that **optimum weight**.

There are ways to work out your optimum weight, based on either your percentage body fat, which can be measured with skinfold callipers (see pages 54–5), or by measuring your wrist girth (see page 40).

Factors affecting optimum body weight

These include:
- height
- sex
- **bone structure**
- **muscle girth.**

For women and men who are the same height, the man would be expected to have a higher optimum weight.

On many age tables and height-to-weight tables Linford Christie would admit to being 'overweight' for his height and age. But no one would accuse him of being fat!

Bone structure and muscle girth play an important part in optimum weight. A person can be 'heavily built' without being overweight (see the definition for 'overfat' on page 43).

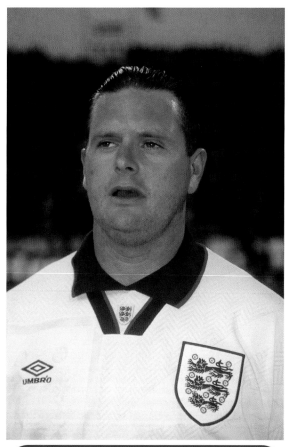

When sportspersons go under or over their optimum body weight, it can often mean they lose speed and endurance – and can get injured as a result

Obesity

Obesity can be caused by some medical conditions, such as a defective thyroid gland, but also by overeating.

Task 1

Give the name of a sport and then give an example of a situation in that sport where being overweight may hamper performance.

Eating disorders

In an effort not to become overweight or obese (in effect the desire is actually to become thin), some people, often teenage girls, suffer from a condition known as **anorexia nervosa.** This is described as a 'chronic illness (without appetite)'. It can be very dangerous.

Bulimia nervosa is a condition in which the person is obsessed with the fear of becoming fat. Bulimics eat vast amounts of food, often in a short space of time, then vomit or use laxatives or other pills to control their weight. Bulimics often feel very guilty after 'bingeing'. Such habits can severely affect their health.

People can also be underweight without suffering either of these conditions.

Weight in sport

Being underweight can affect performance in most sports. Flat race jockeys are often deliberately underweight for their size in order to be able to ride at a prescribed weight for the horse.

In some sports there are weight categories or weight limits within which the participants must fit. Boxing is one which has been fraught with the problems of participants losing weight to come within a certain weight boundary,

In some sports being overweight may not matter, indeed it may help by lowering the centre of gravity, as this bowler shows in the Commonwealth Games

and this has sometimes been blamed for the boxers putting in a poor performance – being literally badly beaten or worse!

Often the manner in which the weight is lost is also important. In the case of boxers, for example, the weight may not be lost gradually by dieting over a period of time. Instead, if it has to be done quickly, it may be by exercising and perhaps wearing sweat suits and/or taking steam baths to lose fluid by sweating (or perspiration), which is not replenished. It may also be lost by taking certain drugs called diuretics.

The results of losing weight quickly in these ways is that the sportsperson can become **dehydrated** and may perform at a lower level than usual.

The use of drugs to affect sports performance will be discussed later in the book (see pages 150–3), but you should already understand that their use is not only against the rules of sports but can be positively dangerous to the health of the sportspeople who take them.

Some individuals are not heavy enough for their sport. These sportspeople need to go on special diets to put weight on, often eating a large amount of kilocalories (calories) to do so.

Task 2

Some sportswomen are sometimes described as being anorexic. Give an example of a sport – not a sportswoman – where you think this might be the case.

Key terms

- **anorexia nervosa**
- **bone structure**
- **bulimia**
- **dehydration**
- **effects of under/overeating**
- **muscle girth**
- **optimum body weight**

The seven factors of a balanced diet

It is important that you understand the nutritional requirements of a balanced diet and the use of each food type.

1 Why carbohydrates?

Carbohydrates are important because they maintain our body's energy stores. There are two types of carbohydrate:

- sugars
- starch.

Bread, pasta, potatoes and rice are some of the main sources of starches, which should form about 47 per cent of our daily energy.

Foods that have been highly processed, such as confectionery and chocolate are often referred to as simple carbohydrates and also contain fat, which is one of the problems with these sources of carbohydrate.

Carbohydrates are stored in the muscle and the liver as **glycogen.** This can be quickly converted into **glucose** and used as energy in the muscle, the brain and other organs.

Starch from complex carbohydrates provides the energy we need when taking part in sport and during our training sessions, so it is important for us to stock up again after our exertions.

2 Why fats?

Fat is important because it provides energy and helps to make other things work, such as fat-soluble **vitamins**. The three types of fat are:

1 saturated fats – normally found in animal fats and are liquid at room temperature; usually called oils
2 polyunsaturated fats
3 monounsaturated fats.

Energy provided from fats should be considerably less than that from complex carbohydrates, probably no more than 30 per cent. The Committee of Medical Aspects of Food and Nutrition Policy (1991) breaks this down further into the three categories:

- saturated fatty acids 10% (11%)
- polyunsaturated fatty acids 6% (6.5%)
- monounsaturated fatty acids 12% (13%).

These figures are percentages of dietary energy. As alcohol also provides energy, the figures in brackets refer to those people who have no energy intake as alcohol. The overall recommendation for those who take alcohol is no more than 5 per cent in the diet.

Task 1

Read the label on a pack of butter or a tub of spread for information on fats. Note the name of the product, the total fat content and how this is broken down into the three categories shown above. Note also the total energy, which may be shown in both kJ and kcal. The energy provided should be shown per 100 g.

3 Why protein?

When **proteins** have been digested, they go via the bloodstream as amino acids into the liver where they are processed for various purposes. The essential use of protein is as a body builder in respect of muscles, and as a repairer of damaged tissue. Protein is important for growth, training and repair when recovering from injury. It can also provide energy (about 15 per cent), but this is of less importance than that provided by carbohydrate and fat. It would only be considered an important source in the case of poor nutrition.

As with carbohydrates and fats, excess protein can be converted and stored as fat.

Protein sources

Protein comes from two types of foods. Two-thirds comes from animal protein, and plant or vegetable protein is the other source. It is therefore not difficult to work out which type of protein is found in which type of food.

- Animal protein is found in meat, poultry and fish, and in dairy products such as milk, cheese and yoghurt. Eggs are also a good source of protein. Saturated fats are also found in these products.

- Plant or vegetable protein is found in pulses (lentils, peas and beans), nuts, bread, potatoes, breakfast cereals, pasta and rice. Some of these foods are also a source of carbohydrate.

Vegans follow a special diet. They eat no animal products at all and get most of their protein from cereals, nuts and pulses.

4 Why vitamins?

We only require vitamins in small quantities and these should be supplied in a normal balanced diet. They are needed for a wide variety of reasons including:

Fresh fruit is a good source of vitamin C

- good vision
- good skin
- red blood cell formation
- healing
- healthy bones and teeth
- blood clotting.

Vitamins come in two groups, those that can be dissolved in water (water soluble) and those that can be dissolved in fat (fat soluble) – one reason for having an adequate supply of fat in our diet.

As vitamins were discovered they were given a letter by which they are known. For example, thiamin became vitamin B1.

Sources of vitamins

- Vitamin A is found in, among other things, milk, cheese, egg yolk, liver and carrots.
- Vitamin B1 is needed to release carbohydrate, and is found in whole grains, nuts and meat.
- Vitamin C is found in fruit and is helpful in healing and fighting infection.
- Vitamin E is found in vegetable oil.

Task 2

Have a good look at your breakfast cereal packet. Write down the names of the vitamins contained in the cereal and what each is needed for.

Key terms

- alcohol
- carbohydrate
- glycogen
- monounsaturated fats
- polyunsaturated fats
- protein
- saturated fats
- sugars and starch
- vitamins

5 Why minerals?

Minerals are inorganic substances that our bodies need for a variety of functions.

Calcium

Calcium is vital to health, especially during growth in childhood and adolescence. It is concerned with the formation and maintenance of bones and teeth, and helps to make the bones strong. Adults reach their peak bone mass around 30–35 years of age and after this there is a gradual decrease. It is important to maintain calcium intake as people get older. Milk, cheese and cereals form a major source of calcium in our diet.

Iron

Iron is an essential mineral which is very important for the blood because of its link with **haemoglobin** and its effect on the oxygen-carrying capacity of the blood and formation of red blood cells (see pages 64–5). A lack of iron can lead to **anaemia** which makes people very tired, irritable and can also affect concentration. Iron is contained in many foods but the iron in meat is absorbed more easily.

Other minerals

Sodium is needed for regulating body water content and is also involved with nerve functioning, while potassium (which is important to the functioning of cells) and magnesium (which assists muscle functioning) are also needed in large amounts. Other minerals are needed in smaller amounts, e.g. zinc and selenium. They are known as trace minerals.

6 Why water?

Water is a means of transport for:

● nutrients

● waste

● hormones.

Water holds oxygen and is the main component of many cells. It also controls the distribution of electrolytes.

| **electrolyte** | a chemical capable of carrying or conducting an electrical charge in solution. The body relies on the presence of electrolytes to carry nerve impulses, to maintain cell metabolism, and other functions. Two common electrolytes in the human system are sodium ions (Na+) and potassium ions (K+). |

Source: *Bodyworks* 5.0

Some isotonic drinks claim to replace electrolytes (or body salts as they are sometimes referred to) after exercise, but a balanced diet will do this naturally.

We have already seen how important water is in terms of body weight. Boxers and jockeys sweat in order to lose weight quickly, and it is thought that this may account for weakness in boxers who find it difficult to 'make the weight'. Boxers and marathon runners need liquid during their exertion in order not to impair their performance and to offset dehydration.

Taking in water is vital for everyone as it makes up about a half of the body's weight and is needed to control body temperature, especially when we are exercising and playing sport.

Marathon runners need to take on water to avoid dehydration

7 Why fibre?

- It adds bulk to food.
- It is important in the functioning of the digestive system.

Fibre (roughage) is in the leaves, stems, roots, tubers, seeds and the fruit of plants. Processing and peeling can result in losing the actual fibre from the food itself.

There are two types of fibre:
- soluble
- insoluble

It is important to eat a variety of food to provide the diet with both types. Wholegrain cereals and wholegrain bread are sources of insoluble fibre, which is required as a bulking agent and to prevent constipation. Oats, fruit and vegetables are sources of soluble fibre needed to reduce blood cholesterol levels.

Some useful nutritional ideas

1 Re-fuel: do not neglect your meals.
2 Make sure you emphasize the complex carbohydrates.
3 If necessary, gradually reduce your intake of fat, starting with visible fat (e.g. the fat you can see on meat).
4 Drink plenty of water and fruit juice.
5 Keep to a balanced diet, and exercise.

Professional sport stars need a carefully thought-out diet to reach high levels of performance

Eating–training–competing

A light meal high in carbohydrate (fat and protein are more difficult to digest) should be taken at least two hours before training or competing, as blood needed for digestion will be diverted to the muscles required for the performance.

Energy and sports activity

Some performers have their own ideas and specialist formulas which they think will provide them with the necessary energy to train and compete – but this in no way compensates for talent and training.

However, a balanced, sensible diet is important. We have seen that we use energy from carbohydrate, fat and protein, but when we use each depends on the type of exercise or sporting activity being undertaken. So when does each come into play?

1 For exercise of a comparatively short nature and high intensity, the energy fuel will come from carbohydrates.
2 For exercise of a longer duration, say up to two hours, but of a moderate intensity, the energy used will come from equal amounts of carbohydrate and fat.
3 For exercise of long duration and higher intensity, for example a marathon, the amount of energy derived from fat stores will increase.

Key terms

- **anaemia**
- **calcium**
- **dehydration**
- **iron**
- **minerals**
- **potassium**
- **sodium**
- **soluble and insoluble fibre**
- **water**

Applying knowledge

Pasta is a good source of carbohydrates

Carbo-loading

Carbo-loading refers to a system that is used mostly by marathon runners, but also by other athletes who take part in ultra-distance events, such as triathlons.

It is designed to make maximum use of the energy resources of the athlete, and a knowledge of the nutrients of a balanced diet will help you to understand how it works.

Suppose it's Sunday, and a runner is running in the London Marathon next Sunday. Today they would go for a very long run, at least 20 miles. What would this do to their energy stores? Well, your answer should be that it depletes them (runs them down very low).

Over the next few days their training programme will reduce in both frequency and intensity allowing them to recover. (We will look at training programmes in some detail later in the book – pages 94–7.)

However, their diet will not be high in carbohydrate, but in protein-rich foods, and you should now know what these include (meat, fish, poultry, dairy products, eggs, pulses, etc.).

You should also know that with this diet their energy stores will remain low. By about Wednesday they will change their diet to include high levels of carbohydrate to completely fill their energy stores in preparation for the race on the Sunday.

Their training will now be over shorter, distances, but at a faster pace, sharpening up their speed for the race.

On the Friday and Saturday before the race the London Marathon is now famous for its 'pasta parties'. And what nutrients does pasta contain? Carbohydrates!

In this way the runners hope that the body's system will be fooled into retaining excessive amounts of carbohydrate, because for the first three days (Sunday, Monday and Tuesday) they have been on low doses of this nutrient.

The aim is to pack in and store as much carbohydrate as possible, which in turn will increase the glycogen stores in the liver and the muscles, ready for the race itself.

Why we need a balanced diet

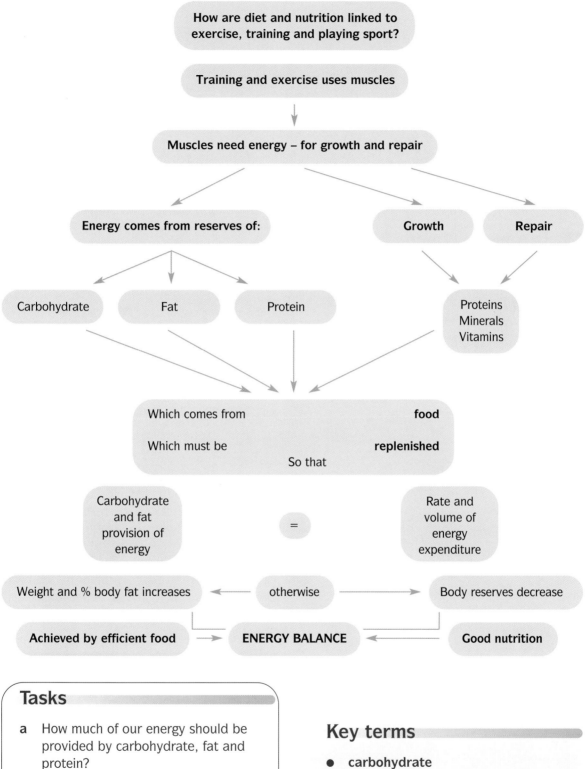

How are diet and nutrition linked to exercise, training and playing sport?

Training and exercise uses muscles

Muscles need energy – for growth and repair

Energy comes from reserves of:

Growth

Repair

Carbohydrate

Fat

Protein

Proteins
Minerals
Vitamins

Which comes from   food

Which must be   replenished

So that

Carbohydrate and fat provision of energy

=

Rate and volume of energy expenditure

Weight and % body fat increases

otherwise

Body reserves decrease

Achieved by efficient food

ENERGY BALANCE

Good nutrition

Tasks

a How much of our energy should be provided by carbohydrate, fat and protein?

b Why is it important to include a regular intake of fibre in our diet?

Key terms

● carbohydrate

● energy

● glycogen

Somatotypes

An often important factor in performance is body build or physique. This can be measured and the result is known as your **somatotype**. There are three somatotypes:

- **endomorph**
- **mesomorph**
- **ectomorph**

and each one of us is likely to be predominant in one of these.

Measurements needed

Various body measurements are needed in order to work out your somatotype and, together with your age and gender, these scores are read from a chart or worked out using a computer program or CD-ROM.

The measurements taken are for:

- height
- weight
- bone size
- muscle girth
- fat.

A score out of seven will then be given in the following categories:

- fatness – endomorphy
- muscularity – mesomorphy
- linearity (thinness) – ectomorphy.

So a person's somatotype might be: 2:6:2. This would mean 2/7 for fat; 6/7 for muscle; and 2/7 for thinness. Investigations have shown that this is a good somatotype for many sportspeople.

Somatotypes in sport

Once the somatotype is known, it can be plotted on a somato chart (see page 57).

Studies have been carried out which show that sportspeople from certain sports seem to group together on the somato chart. For example, most sportspeople are mesomorphs, but some – such as marathon runners and flat race jockeys – are closer to the ectomorph end of the scale.

Dr W. H. Sheldon in America carried out much of the early work on these investigations, but R. W. Parnell did further work in the UK. More recent studies have shown that some sportspeople can score off the charts, perhaps even as high as 9!

One explanation for this might be that sportspeople are actually getting bigger. The Olympic Games men's 100 metres final may bear this out, as 30 years ago the competitors were similarly built, but were what might be termed 'a size smaller'.

Changing body composition

Body composition is to a large extent passed on through the genes from parent to child, but in exceptional circumstances it can be changed.

One way in which it can be changed is by dieting very severely – for example, in cases of anorexia nervosa (see page 45). Following a severe training programme might have the opposite effect, as can sometimes be seen with body-builders. Taking drugs, either to lose weight or to put weight on, can also bring about such changes.

Somatotype can be changed

Measuring your somatotype

In order to measure your somatotype you will need to know a little bit about the structure or anatomy of your body, and its function or physiology.

As you take the measurements, make a note of them in your exercise book and then copy them out neatly on your profile sheet, PF1. (Some other measurements are also asked for. Record these at the same time, as they will be needed for later tests.)

Remember that you are probably at the most difficult age to measure somatotype as you may be growing rapidly and the charts are either designed for younger children or adults. However, the most important thing is to learn from the process.

You will need

- pen or pencil
- profile sheet (PF1)
- tape showing feet and inches and metres/centimetres, or stadiometer
- scales showing pounds and kilograms.

What to do

1 Insert your name, age and the date on which you are doing the tests.
2 Measure your height in feet and inches.
3 Measure your height in metres (needed for later test).
4 Measure your weight in pounds.
5 Measure your weight in kilograms (needed for later test).

Note: Take your measurements in your PE kit but without shoes.

Some sportspeople struggle against weight problems

Key terms

- **ectomorph**
- **endomorph**
- **mesomorph**
- **somatotype**

Ex-boxer Frank Bruno, a great example of a mesomorph

Muscles that work in pairs like this are known as **antagonistic muscles.** When these muscles work they either bend (caused by the biceps and known as **flexion**) or straighten (caused by the triceps and known as **extension**) the arm. When a muscle works, or is contracted, it bulges.

Task 1

a   Try 'flexing' your bicep. In this way you can work out which muscle is working. Now try to make the tricep bulge, what happens to the elbow joint?

b   Which of these muscles bends the arm? Which one straightens it?

Measuring fat

Most of the body is covered just beneath the skin with a substance that we call fat. This fat tends to be thicker in young children and women, and can vary between members of the same sex and at different parts of the body. As men get older they tend to increase in fat in the lower abdomen, while women increase fat on the thighs and buttocks as well.

Fat is very good at conserving heat, so thin people feel the cold much more than fat people, and between the sexes females generally feel the cold less than males, as they have an extra layer. An example of this was in a canoeing tragedy when all the boys died of hypothermia, whilst all but one of the girls survived.

In order to find your somatotype, it is necessary to measure your body fat, or skinfolds as they are known, at three sites on the right side of your body. A fourth site is required for a further test.

The skinfold sites

Biceps and triceps

The biceps and the triceps are both muscles. The biceps are found in the upper arm at the front, and the triceps in the upper arm at the back. These two muscles work together, or in pairs.

Subscapula (below the scapula)

The scapula is a bone commonly called the shoulder blade. It forms a **joint** (see page 56) with the humerus, which is the bone at the top of the arm.

Supra-iliac (above the iliac crest)

The supra-iliac is a prominent point found just above the hip-bone, or the crest (top) of the ilium.

Taking skinfold measurements

Skinfold measurements are taken by raising the skinfold with the thumb and forefinger of the left hand (for a right-handed person). Be sure not to lift muscle and fat! Open the callipers by gently squeezing the 'trigger' of the calliper with the forefinger of the right hand. Put the calliper over the skinfold and release gradually with the trigger finger. Measurements are read in millimetres.

Finding the sites

The over tricep measurement, as it is known, is taken halfway between the tip of the shoulder and the point of the elbow at the back of the arm (you might well call it your 'funny bone').

If possible, use a ruler to measure accurately between these two points.

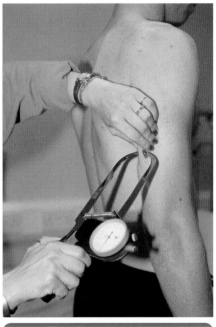

The tricep measurement

The bicep measurement is taken at a point equal to the tricep measurement but on the bicep side of the arm.

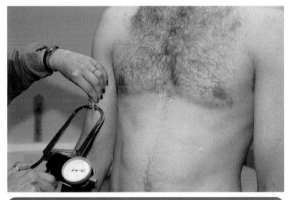

The bicep measurement

Remember to exclude muscle from the measurement; it may help to lock the elbow joint while the reading is taken.

The scapula is a triangular shape, and the skinfold is taken at the bottom of the triangle, which is why it is known as the subscapula skinfold. The skinfold should run downwards and outwards towards the ribs.

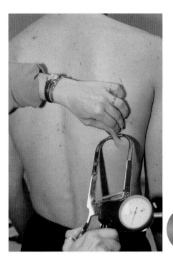

The subscapula measurement

The next site is the supra-iliac – just above the hip-bone. Raise the skinfold as before, one or two inches above the hip-bone, so that the skinfold runs forward and slightly downwards.

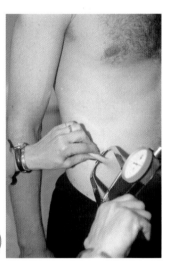

The supra-iliac measurement

Task 2

Take each skinfold measurement three times, and record the average score.

Key terms

- **antagonistic muscles**
- **extension**
- **flexion**
- **skinfolds**

Taking bone measurements

Finding the sites

The humerus is the bone at the top of the arm. At one end it forms the shoulder joint with the scapula and at the other it forms the elbow joint with two bones in the lower arm. One of these bones is called the ulna. It can be remembered as the one that is 'underneath.' The other bone is called the radius. The humerus has a joint at each end. So what is the definition of a joint?

joint	a place where two or more bones meet

The femur is the thigh-bone. It is located between the knee and the hip and it is the largest bone in the body. Like the humerus it has a large globular head, or ball, at one end, which fits into a socket in the hip, forming the hip joint.

Below the knee joint is the tibia, commonly called the shin bone, and there is a more slender bone on the outside of the tibia called the fibula. The tibia takes the full weight of the leg and is the one that forms the knee joint.

Task 3

a   Bend your elbow to a right angle. Use a condyle calliper to measure the widest point across the elbow: this is a measurement across the elbow: this is a measurement across the condyles of the humerus.

b   Repeat the process with the femur.

These are the points you must measure to get your somatotype bone measurements. Take each measurement in centimetres three times and record the average score.

Taking muscle girth measurements

Muscle girth is the size around the muscle taken at the widest part when the muscle is flexed. In the case of the bicep, the upper arm (humerus) should be held horizontal, and it should make a right angle with the forearm (ulna).

For the gastrocnemius (the muscle at the back of the lower leg), the subject should stand with the feet slightly apart, and the measurement is again taken around the widest part with the muscle flexed.

The tape should only make light contact with the skin, and again the measurements are taken in centimetres.

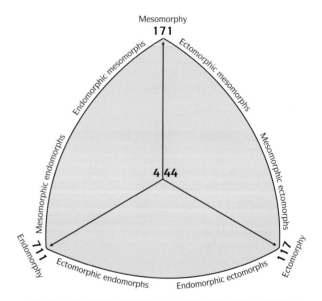

A blank somato chart

Finding your somatotype

Once all the measurements are taken you can find your somatotype either by using a computer program or reading it from a chart (see page 95 in the Teacher's Resource File).

Once you have worked out your somatotype, you can plot it onto a somato chart like the one shown above.

Task 4

Once you have plotted your own somatotype on your chart, exchange scores with other students and plot their scores on your chart.

Task 5

Now you have plotted your group scores on your chart, can you spot any trends?

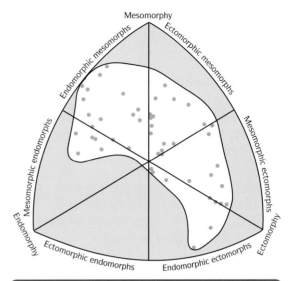

Somatotype distribution of college sportsmen

Somatotypes in sport

Research has shown that certain body types are found in certain sports, and even within some sports the player's body shape is relevant.

This may not be too surprising if we think of, say, athletics. We would not expect the throwers (who are predominantly mesomorphic endomorphs) to be the same shape as the high jumpers (who are predominantly ectomorphic mesomorphs).

So what is a mesomorphic endomorph? Basically it means that for a thrower, the highest rating is in mesomorphy (muscle) and the second highest rating is in endomorphy (fat). The high jumper would have the highest rating in ectomorphy (linearity/thinness) and the second highest rating in mesomorphy (muscle).

On the track, the sprinters tend to be more mesomorphic than the distance runners and research has shown that the sprinters of today are both taller and more muscular than those of 30 years ago.

The two charts on this page compare the somatotypes of two groups of students at an English college. One group represented the college in their sport – i.e. they were keen sportspeople – while the other group played no sport at all.

If you compare the two charts, you can see that the sportspeople tended to be more mesomorphic while those who did no sport tended to be more ectomorphic.

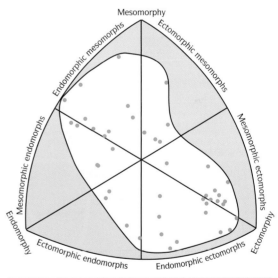

Somatotype distribution of college non-sportsmen

Key terms

- ectomorphy
- endomorphy
- femur
- fibula
- gastrocnemius
- humerus
- mesomorphy
- radius
- ulna

Cardiovascular fitness

cardiac	of the heart
vascular	of or containing vessels for conveying blood

Cardiovascular fitness is the ability to exercise the entire body for long periods of time. It requires a strong heart and clear blood vessels to supply the muscles with plenty of oxygen via the blood.

Cardiovascular fitness has some benefit to all sportspeople, indeed to everyone, as it concerns the fitness of the most important muscle in the body – the heart!

Task 1

List five sports or activities that involve cardiovascular activity. For example: athletics, running 1500 m.

The heart

The heart is a muscular pump. It is divided into two halves by a central partition called the septum. Each half is then also divided by valves into an **atrium** (auricle) above (a good way to remember this is '*A' for above*) and a **ventricle** below. We therefore have a right and left atrium and a right and left ventricle.

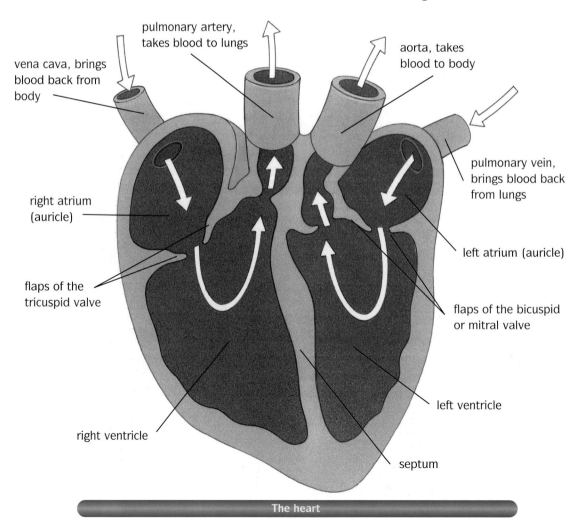

pulmonary artery, takes blood to lungs

vena cava, brings blood back from body

aorta, takes blood to body

pulmonary vein, brings blood back from lungs

right atrium (auricle)

left atrium (auricle)

flaps of the tricuspid valve

flaps of the bicuspid or mitral valve

right ventricle

left ventricle

septum

The heart

The vena cava brings venous blood (deoxygenated blood) from the body into the right atrium, but venous blood is also brought back from the heart walls by the small coronary sinus.

The venous blood collects in the right atrium and then it passes through an opening between the atrium and the ventricle by going through a valve with three cusps called the tricuspid valve. It then arrives in the right ventricle. It is then pushed through the semi-lunar valves into the pulmonary **artery** and goes on into the lungs.

Arterial blood (oxygenated blood) from the lungs passes through the pulmonary **vein** and is collected in the left atrium. It then passes through an opening between the left atrium and the left ventricle which is guarded by a valve with two cusps called the bicuspid or mitral valve. It then arrives in the left ventricle.

When the heart contracts it is called systole. This is when blood is pumped around the body. The blood in the right ventricle goes into the pulmonary artery on its way to the lungs, while the blood in the left ventricle passes through the semi-lunar valves into the aorta and goes on its way around the body.

The left ventricle is much thicker than the right ventricle so that the force of the arterial blood is much greater than that of the venous blood. The reason for this is the difference in the distances that the two streams have to travel – one just the small distance to the lungs and the other all around the body.

When you have your blood pressure monitored, the results come as two figures. Systole gives the higher figure when blood pressure is at its maximum as the heart contracts. Blood pressure falls between heartbeats and the measurement of this gives the lower figure. Some experts say that blood pressure is the most important aspect of fitness that we should monitor; it is a very important factor affecting participation and performance. We will look at blood pressure in more detail on page 63.

Key terms

- aorta
- atrium
- bicuspid or mitral valve
- cardiovascular fitness
- pulmonary artery
- pulmonary vein
- semi-lunar valves
- tricuspid valve
- vena cava
- ventricle

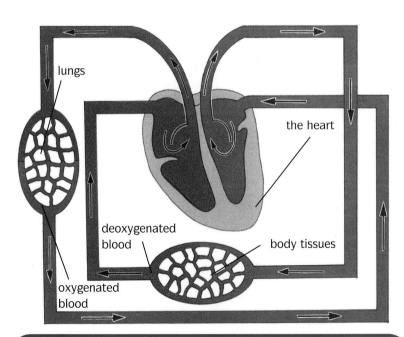

lungs

the heart

deoxygenated blood

body tissues

oxygenated blood

Double circulatory pump system – pulmonary circulation carries blood from the heart to the lungs and back again; systemic circulation carries blood from the heart to all parts of the body except the lungs, and back again. The valves prevent the blood flowing backwards

Heart rate

We are not directly able to control our **heart rate** because it is under the control of the involuntary nervous system. One group of nerves (the sympathetic) accelerates the heart and the other group (the parasympathetic) slows the heart down. Both, however, are controlled by the cardiac centre, which is in the brain.

Arteries

The wall of the heart is supplied with blood from two small vessels called the coronary **arteries** which are the first branches given off from the aorta. These can become blocked by blood clots and when this happens blood supplied to part of the heart wall is cut off, resulting in sudden death.

The structure of arteries, **veins** and **capillaries** is different. The arteries have a relatively thick wall. Most arteries and arterioles (very small arteries) carry arterial or oxygenated blood away from the heart. This is why they pulsate as the heart beats. The channel the blood flows through, called the **lumen**, can widen to allow an increase in blood supply through arteries. This happens during exercise to get more blood more quickly to the working muscles. Arteries are more elastic than veins and also have higher pressure. The pulmonary arteries are different. They carry venous blood from the heart to the lungs. _Any vessel leaving the heart is called an artery, even if it is carrying venous blood_.

Veins

Veins carry venous or deoxygenated blood to the heart and have much thinner walls than arteries. They contain many valves, which keep venous blood flowing to the heart, and avoid the possibility of blood flowing backwards.

Capillaries
the smallest of the blood vessels, very thin walls (one cell thick)

Veins
thin walls, less elastic than arteries, blood is at lower pressure than in arteries, have valves, carry blood _to_ the heart

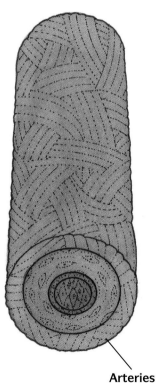

Arteries
thick walls, more elastic than veins, pulsate, have no valves, carry blood _away from_ the heart

The structure of arteries, veins and capillaries is different

There is a tendency for this to happen because venous blood is often flowing upwards against gravity. Veins rarely pulsate. They are less elastic than arteries and carry blood at a lower pressure. The pulmonary veins, which leave the lungs on the way to the heart, are different from other veins. They carry arterial or oxygenated blood. <u>Any vessel *entering* the heart is called a vein even though it may be carrying arterial blood.</u>

Task 2

Make two lists, one titled 'arteries' and the other 'veins'. Then list the points about each. For example, arteries work at higher pressure.

Capillaries

Capillaries are microscopic vessels that link the arteries with the veins. At one end, they carry arterial blood which transfers supplies of oxygen and nutrients to the muscles. At the other end, capillaries pick up waste and carry venous blood into the veins as they pass through the system.

Cardiac cycle

The whole action of the heart and **circulatory system** is called the cardiac cycle.

Facts about smoking

The arteries need to be clear and free from obstruction in order to carry blood and supplies to the working muscles, but these passageways can be blocked by lipids or fibrous tissue which can be caused by smoking. This condition is known as atherosclerosis.

As was mentioned earlier, the heart rate is controlled by the sympathetic nervous system. Nicotine, one of the main components of tobacco, affects this system, increasing the heart rate and raising the blood pressure.

Smoking, at any age, causes a wide variety of health problems

Other conditions associated with smoking include coronary heart disease (CHD) or heart attack, which is the main cause of death from smoking, and strokes, which affect the brain and which may affect the person's speech and/or cause paralysis. Smokers also run higher risks during complicated operations.

There are two types of smoking:

- active – when a person actually smokes
- passive – when a non-smoker is affected by the smoke from another person's cigarette.

Smoking in western Europe is decreasing, although it is on the increase among young women.

It is said that the risk of a heart attack is decreased after the smoker has stopped smoking for one year.

Task 3

Explain the importance of the capillaries in the circulatory system.

Key terms

- **arterial blood**
- **arteries**
- **arterioles**
- **capillaries**
- **cardiac cycle**
- **heart rate**
- **veins**
- **venous blood**

The second pressure will be your diastolic pressure. This is when the ventricle is in its relaxation phase. Average pressures at this point would be between 60 and 80 mmHg.

In old age the blood vessel walls become less elastic (this is called hardening of the arteries) and the small vessels do not expand to let through the blood pumped from the heart. This means that resistance to the flow of blood is increased, and this means that blood pressure rises.

People with high blood pressure are said to have hypertension.

Heartbeat

If you listen to a heartbeat with a stethoscope you hear two sounds. The first is called systole, and it occurs when ventricles have contracted and push the blood into the arteries. The actual sound is caused by the cuspid valves closing. The second sound is called diastole and this happens when the atria contract, pushing blood down into the ventricles. This sound is caused by semi-lunar valves closing between the ventricles and the arteries.

Fitness and heart disease

As our fitness improves, the number of small capillaries in our heart increases. If a heart attack due to a blockage occurs, it is the area of the damage that is critical. In a fit person the amount of damage is likely to be more limited than in an unfit person.

Being a football manager can be extremely stressful – Joe Kinnear had a stress-related heart attack when managing Wimbledon F.C.

Why do we need to take our blood pressure?

If you go to a doctor for a check up, you are very likely to have your blood pressure checked. The doctor or nurse will take your blood pressure using a sphygmomanometer – a blood pressure meter.

The results of the test will come in two figures. The first will be your systolic pressure, or the pressure of the blood when it is being pumped into the arteries by the contraction of the left ventricle of the heart. Average pressures would be between 110 and 135 mmHg (this stands for millimetres of mercury – the units for measuring blood pressure).

Task 4

Use a blood pressure meter to take your blood pressure. Lie on the floor or sit perfectly still for 30 seconds before taking a reading. Then stand up and jump ten times in the air and retake your blood pressure.

More about blood pressure

- *Systolic blood pressure* is the maximum pressure of the blood. It occurs at the contraction of the ventricles. It rises during activity or excitement and falls during sleep.

- *Diastolic blood pressure* is the pressure of the blood during the relaxation phase between heartbeats. It depends mainly on the elasticity of the arteries and the quality of the vessels.

- *Pulse pressure* is the difference between systolic and diastolic blood pressures.

Blood pressure varies with age, sex, altitude, muscular development and according to a person's state of stress or tiredness. It is usually lower in women, and it is low in childhood and high in old age.

Abnormal blood pressure

- systolic persistently above 140 mmHg
- diastolic above 100 mmHg
- pulse pressure constantly above 50 or below 30

What can I do to reduce the risk of high blood pressure?

There is a lot you can do to help to keep blood pressure at a normal level.

1 Check your weight.

2 Limit your alcohol consumption.

3 Avoid smoking – it will make your blood pressure worse and damages the heart and blood vessels.

4 In some people too much salt may unbalance the body chemistry and affect blood pressure.

5 Avoid situations that cause stress, anxiety or worry.

6 Exercise regularly – this will help to control stress, keep your blood pressure normal and your whole system in good shape.

Key terms

- **diastole, diastolic**
- **pulse pressure**
- **stress**
- **systole, systolic**

Testing blood pressure is part of a general medical check-up

The composition of blood

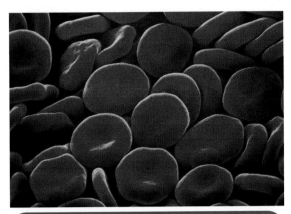

Red blood cells (erythrocytes) carry supplies around the body

The blood is really the transport system of the body, as it carries materials from one organ to another. It takes oxygen from the lungs to the heart and then to the tissues. It takes carbon dioxide from the tissues to the heart and then to the lungs. It also takes soluble food from the intestines and waste products from the kidneys.

Red blood cells

If people are ill they often have a blood test. To a hepatologist (a specialist in this field) looking through a microscope, blood looks quite different from the red liquid that we know. Millions of cells float in a yellowish liquid called plasma. Most of these are disc-shaped and orange but in a large mass they appear red and are called red blood cells or erythrocytes. The pigment that gives the cells their colour is called **haemoglobin** and it attracts oxygen. It picks up oxygen in the lungs and delivers it to the tissues. This is very important with regard to health and fitness.

High cell count

One cubic millimetre of healthy blood contains about five million red cells, but this can vary considerably. People who are born and live in mountainous or high altitude regions (such as areas in the African country of Kenya), where there is less oxygen in the air, have a higher cell count (or 'blood count') because the blood has to be extra efficient at picking up oxygen. People who live at altitude may have as much as two more litres of blood than people who are the same size as them but who live at sea level. Athletes from these areas often do exceptionally well in distance races, as we see from the Kenyan results in events such as 5000 metres, 10,000 metres, steeplechase and marathon running. Other athletes go to train in these areas in order to improve their ability to cope better when they return to lower levels for competition. A controversial and illegal procedure called 'blood doping' is sometimes used, which makes use of this knowledge (see also page 77).

Kenyan athletes, who train at high altitude, have been extremely successful in distance races

Task 1

a   In a short paragraph, try to explain what problems may face athletes not used to competing at high altitude when competing for the first time at such a venue.

b   What type of event might cause these athletes most problems?

Low cell count

A low cell count causes you to be breathless and lacking in energy. This condition is known as **anaemia** and it has many causes. If you lose a lot of blood you will become anaemic. Haemoglobin contains iron and a lack of iron will cause anaemia. This can be rectified by taking tablets containing iron, or by eating foods rich in iron, such as liver or spinach.

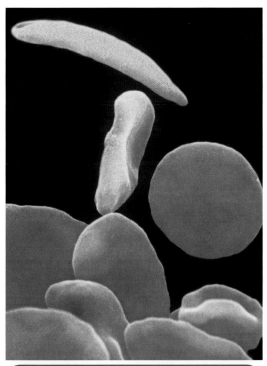

Sickle cell anaemia causes cells to become distorted and crescent shaped

Red blood cells are made from red bone marrow and if this is not working properly, again, anaemia will result. This condition can now often be cured with a bone marrow transplant.

Sickle cell anaemia

This is a special sort of anaemia because the red blood cells become distorted and crescent-shaped. This is an inherited disease passed on through the genes of the parents, but the gene has to be present in both parents for the child to inherit the disease. Sickle cell anaemia is most common in West Africa and some parts of Europe, such as Greece.

Blood plasma

Blood plasma is a pale straw-coloured liquid consisting of 90% water. It contains inorganic salts, especially substances such as sodium chloride (common salt) and **calcium.** It also contains substances such as sugar (glucose), antibodies, urea and other waste products. The plasma also contains substances that are important for maintaining circulation between the cells and the tissues – these are called plasma proteins.

Key terms

- **altitude**
- **anaemia**
- **blood plasma**
- **haemoglobin**
- **red blood cells (erythrocytes)**

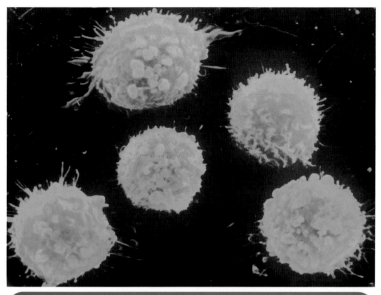

White blood cells (leukocytes) form part of the body's defence system

White blood cells

As well as the red blood cells in blood there are also transparent cells, which are called the white blood cells or leukocytes. These have an important function as the defence system of the body, as they can destroy pathogens, which can cause disease. Some of these cells completely engulf bacteria or viruses in the blood and digest them, while others destroy the pathogens with chemicals called antibodies.

One way of keeping healthy is by encouraging white cells to produce more antibodies than are needed to combat pathogens, making them immune from attack. A vaccine is actually a mild dose of a particular disease, which encourages the white cells to produce more antibodies to protect against further attack. Sometimes the immunity is permanent; other vaccines are only temporary.

Sometimes it is necessary to lower a person's immune system, and tablets are given to kill off some of the white blood cells. An example of this are operations such as heart, kidney or liver transplants, where the body's defence system might cause a transplanted organ to be rejected.

Blood platelets

Blood platelets are formed in the red bone marrow and are concerned with the production of a substance called thrombokinase, which is essential for the clotting of blood. In fact blood is the first line of defence in the repair of an open wound. This is brought about by a series of chemical reactions. When giving First Aid we can assist this process by pushing together the edges of a wound and compressing firmly with a sterile pad.

A decreased number of platelets in the blood can be an extremely serious condition, for example when undergoing an operation.

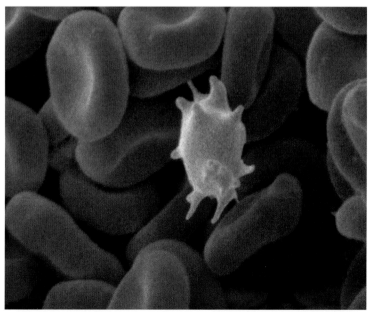

A blood platelet

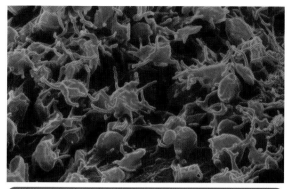

Platelets stick together to block cuts

Platelets and clotting

Platelets are tiny specialized particles that are activated whenever blood clotting or repair to a vessel is necessary. Although they are often called cells, they are really parts of other cells. They are made in bone marrow and are much smaller than red blood cells. A drop of blood contains some 15 million platelets.

When a blood vessel is cut, platelets rush to the site of the injury and swell into odd, irregular shapes. They become sticky and block the cut, acting as a plug. If the platelets cannot cope with a large cut, a signal is sent out to start clotting by releasing a hormone called serotonin. This causes the blood vessels to contract and this reduces the flow of blood. Many factors are involved in this conversion. As well as stopping bleeding, clotting also helps to build new tissue.

Haemophilia

Haemophilia is the best known of all clotting diseases. It is an inherited disease from which only men suffer, although women may be carriers and pass it on to their sons. It is actually relatively rare and occurs because a clotting factor is missing. Even a slight injury to a haemophiliac can cause very serious bleeding, often requiring a blood transfusion.

Today, blood transfusions and injections of the missing factor, which can be extracted from plasma, give haemophiliacs the chance of a more normal life.

Blood testing

Blood can be tested in a laboratory to screen for all these conditions. With a CBC, or complete blood count, the different types of cell can be counted electronically. This allows doctors to know how many red cells, white cells and platelets a person has, and see whether these numbers are within the required range. If they are outside the range it could indicate some form of illness or dietary problem.

Task 2

a   Write down the odd one out of each group and explain why it is different.

   i   aorta
   ii   capillary
   iii ventricle
   iv   vein

   i   red cells
   ii   haemoglobin
   iii platelets
   iv   arteries

   i   pulmonary vein
   ii   ventricle
   iii atrium
   iv   septum

   From the above words, choose the correct answer to the following questions.

b   What is the name given to the clotting agent of the blood?

c   What is the name given to the pigment which carries oxygen in the blood?

Key terms

- **antibodies**
- **blood platelets (thrombocytes)**
- **haemophilia**
- **immune system**
- **pathogens**
- **thrombokinase**
- **white blood cells (leukocytes)**

How training and fitness affect the heart

Heart rate or pulse rate

This is the number of times the heart beats per minute. **Heart rate** is caused by the actual impact of the blood on the arteries as the heart contracts. In a trained athlete it is likely to be lower than in an unfit person, and it is therefore heart rate that is used to indicate a person's fitness level.

However, heart rate can vary considerably from person to person and even within the same individual, so it is difficult to say what is a normal heart rate, but 72 beats per minute (b.p.m.) is often thought of as being average. A trained athlete, like Olympic rower Steven Redgrave, could have a resting pulse rate as low as 40 b.p.m., while a quite normal person could have a resting pulse rate of 100 b.p.m. The resting pulse rate could also be affected by age, sex, size, **posture,** eating, emotion, body temperature, environmental factors and most important, smoking!

Maximum pulse rate

It is thought that maximum pulse rate is not affected by training. It can be worked out by the formula:

$$220 - age = maximum\ pulse\ rate$$

This is the same for men and women. For example, for a male or female aged 20, the maximum pulse rate is:

$$220 - 20 = 200\ beats\ per\ minute\ (b.p.m.)$$

Stroke volume

This is the amount of blood pumped by the heart per beat.

At rest, **stroke volume** may be 85 ml, but when exercising it could go up to 130 ml.

Cardiac output

This is the amount of blood pumped by the heart in one minute.

Cardiac output is governed by the heart rate (pulse) and the stroke volume.

$$cardiac\ output = stroke\ volume \times heart\ rate$$

When a person trains regularly their stroke volume will increase, both at rest and at work. On the other hand, the heart rate does not increase it decreases, so the heart becomes more efficient! Training increases the heart muscle in size, thickness and strength, the chambers increases in volume and the whole heart gets bigger.

The heart of a man is generally about 10% bigger than that of a woman.

The cardiac muscle

As we now know, the cardiac muscle forms the wall of the heart and its contractions are beyond our control. So we must remember that the cardiac muscle is involuntary. The cardiac muscle is made up of fibres which interlace and this helps the passage of the nervous impulses. These impulses are controlled by a centre in the brain which regulates the rate and force of the heartbeat. The remarkable feature of the cardiac muscle is that it *never tires!*

Measuring cardiovascular fitness

Maximum oxygen uptake (VO₂ max.)

The best measure of cardiovascular fitness is called maximum oxygen uptake or **VO₂ max.**

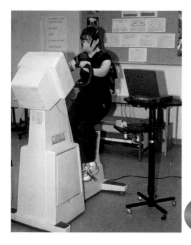

The VO$_2$ max. test

The bleep test

This measures the ability of the heart, lungs, blood and the blood vessels to transport oxygen to the muscles. This test needs specialist equipment using what is known as a Douglass bag. This catches all the oxygen expired by an athlete while they are undertaking a strenuous test on a cycle ergometer.

Physical work capacity (PWC 170)

Another test is of the amount of work required in relation to your age, height and weight, to get your pulse rate up to 170 b.p.m. This is known as your physical work capacity, or PWC 170.

This test can also take place using a cycle ergometer, but this time your pulse is taken at regular intervals and the intensity of the workload set on the cycle is increased accordingly.

Bleep test

Another test that is frequently used is the 'bleep test' in which you are required to run 20 metre shuttles, in time with a bleep, which gradually gets faster. This is a test to exhaustion. You can also measure your pulse rate and blood pressure.

Tasks

a   If you had a normal heart rate of 72 b.p.m., work out how many times your heart would beat in one hour.

b   Now work out how many times your heart would beat if your normal heart rate was 56 b.p.m.

c   Work out the total difference in the number of beats in a day.

Key terms

- bleep test
- cardiac output
- heart rate
- involuntary muscle
- maximum oxygen uptake (VO$_2$ max.)
- PWC 170
- stroke volume

The PWC 170 test

Tips about exercise and caution

Before starting a Personal Exercise Programme (PEP) it is important to assess your state of readiness by completing a Physical Activity Readiness Questionaire or PARQ. This will assess your health history and highlight any medical problems. Some people may need a medical check up first, according to age and medical history. Then they should find an exercise that suits them, starting slowly and building up gradually. They should exercise until pleasantly tired but not exhausted, as too much may do more harm than good. With the right level of activity you may be breathless but you should not be speechless!

Task

Measure your resting and working pulse rates and insert them in the appropriate place on your profile sheet (PF1).

Resting pulse rate

This is the heart rate at rest. Resting pulse rates vary, but will normally be between 60–80 b.p.m. A person who exercises regularly may have a resting pulse of 50–60 b.p.m. Therefore we can see that one effect of regular exercise is that the resting heart rate will be slower. We can also see that the heart of a fit person will beat far fewer times, therefore it will be much more efficient, causing less stress to be put on the heart.

Measuring the pulse

The pulse can be measured at a number of sites but the two most common ones are the carotid pulse and the radial pulse. The carotid pulse is found by putting the index and middle fingers to one side of the Adam's apple (larynx) and applying slight pressure.

The radial pulse is found, again with the index and middle fingers, but this time on the palm side of the wrist, just above the thumb.

Measuring the carotid pulse

Measuring the radial pulse

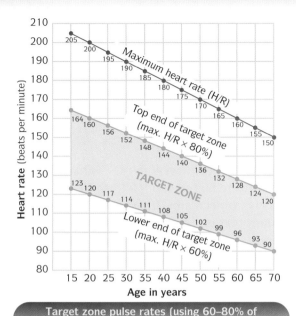

Target zone pulse rates (using 60–80% of max. H/R)

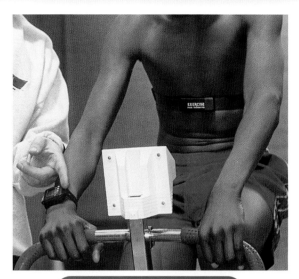

A pulsemeter gives a very accurate measurement of pulse rate

Working pulse rate

The working pulse rate (or working heart rate) is a measurement of pulse rate taken immediately after exercise.

This is an accurate guide to the intensity (how hard) the heart has been working. A target range (or target zone) can be set for the heart rate to reach during exercise, and this can be worked out by the formula below.

> maximum heart rate (H/R) = 220 – age
>
> lower end of target zone = max. H/R × 60%
>
> top end of target zone = max. H/R × 80%

For example, the target H/R for a 15-year-old would be:

> 220 – 15 = 205
>
> 205 × 60% = 123
>
> 205 × 80% = 164

Therefore the target zone is:

> 123–164 b.p.m.

Using a pulsemeter

A special instrument called a heart rate monitor, pulsemeter or pulse monitor, can be used to measure your pulse very accurately while you are working.

It takes your pulse electronically with electrodes attached to your chest and displays them on a monitor strapped to your wrist like a watch.

Using resting pulse to work out the target zone

The table below shows an accurate guide to the working pulse rates required during exercise in order to improve fitness. These are based on resting pulse rates and take into account the fitness of athletes who are already in training and may have already brought down their resting pulse rate.

Resting pulse	Working pulse *Beginner*	Working pulse *Athlete*
Below 50	135–140	145–150
51–70	141–145	151–155
Above 71	146–150	156–160

Key terms

- carotid pulse
- radial pulse
- resting pulse rate
- target range or zone
- working pulse rate

The respiratory system – the lungs

Breathing in

When we breathe in, the cycle starts with the ribs lifting upwards and outwards. This is caused by the contraction of the **intercostal muscles** which are situated between the ribs.

There is also movement in the body as the **diaphragm** (a sheet of muscle and tough fibres which cuts off the chest region from the rest of the body cavity) contracts, changing from a dome shape to a flatter sheet. It relaxes when we breathe out, moving upwards back to a dome shape.

The thorax is lined with the pleural membrane, which is stuck to the thorax and also to the outside of the lungs. The pleural membrane attaches the lungs to the thorax so that when you breathe in, the chest enlarges and pulls the lungs outwards. The pressure in the lungs is reduced and air drawn in through the nose and/or mouth rushes in to compensate.

The air passes into the lungs down a tube called the trachea. This is made up of gristle-like rings of **cartilage.** There are plates of cartilage at the top of the trachea which widen it at the point commonly called the Adam's apple. This is actually the larynx or 'voice box', which is protected by a flap of skin called the epiglottis. This closes when we swallow in order to prevent food from going down the trachea. Occasionally this doesn't happen and we have all experienced the feeling of choking when food 'goes down the wrong way'.

At the bottom of the trachea are two branches called the bronchi, through which air passes into either lung. Smaller and smaller branches, called bronchioles, extend out from the bronchi and at the very ends of these they form tiny sacs called alveoli.

Alveoli

The alveoli would cover over 55 square metres if they were flattened out and so they have a massive surface area. They give the lungs their spongy texture.

The linings of the alveoli are very thin and only work well when they are moist and clean. A healthy person has a very efficient mechanism for ensuring this. When air is breathed in through the nose, it is:

- *filtered* by the hairs at the entrance to the nose and by mucus which is a sticky substance
- *warmed* by blood vessels passing close to the lining of the nose
- *moistened* by water vapour.

Inside the trachea and the bronchi the cleaning process continues to go on, as these tubes are lined with microscopic hairs, which are also covered with mucus.

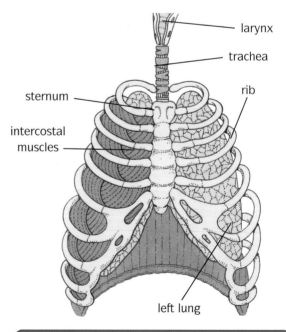

The mechanism for breathing

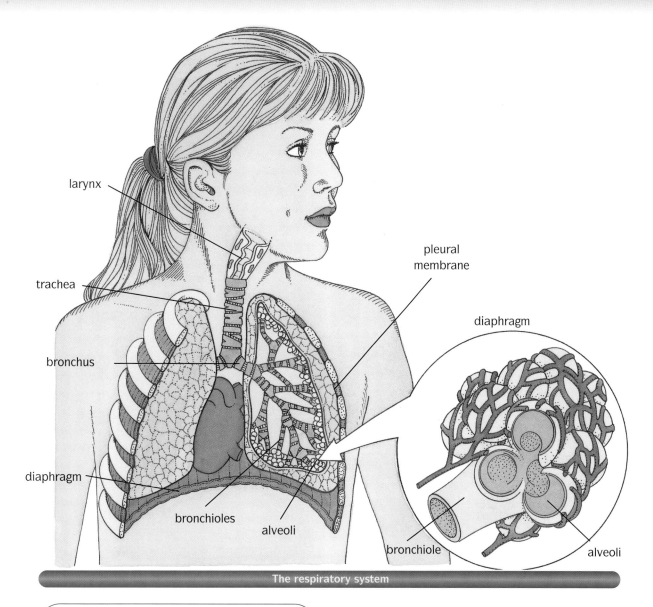

larynx

trachea

bronchus

diaphragm

bronchioles

alveoli

pleural
membrane

diaphragm

bronchiole

alveoli

The respiratory system

Task 1

a List the following five words in the order that breathed in air would go through them:

- bronchi
- larynx
- alveoli
- trachea
- bronchioles.

b Explain three major functions of the nasal passages.

c Describe what happens to the ribs when we breathe in.

Key terms

- **alveoli**
- **bronchi**
- **bronchioles**
- **diaphragm**
- **epiglottis**
- **intercostal muscles**
- **larynx**
- **pleural membrane**
- **respiratory system**
- **thorax**
- **trachea**

Gaseous exchange

The alveoli are in very close contact with the blood capillaries, which contain red blood cells and haemoglobin. We have already seen (on page 64) that haemoglobin carries oxygen and at this point in the circulatory system it attracts the oxygen in the alveoli. Whilst the oxygen is taken in, carbon dioxide is given out, or exchanged, into the alveoli and is then breathed out. (With training, more alveoli become available for gaseous exchange.)

The oxygen picked up by the haemoglobin is transported (through the circulatory system) around the body in the red blood cells via the bloodstream, before being deposited in the living cells. A series of chemical reactions (called tissue respiration) then takes place which combines glucose (from the food we eat) with the oxygen to release energy, along with the waste products of carbon dioxide and water. The energy released is used to help us move, grow and keep warm.

Giving expired air resuscitation (EAR)

It is essential for oxygen to be present because without it these processes would not work, and as carbon dioxide is poisonous if it builds up, this exchange is crucial for our survival.

A more technical way to show this process is:

glucose + oxygen → energy + carbon dioxide + water

So the respiratory system has two main jobs:

1   to get oxygen into the body
2   to get carbon dioxide out of the body.

What we breathe

As well as breathing in oxygen, we also breathe out a lot of oxygen. This is most important when we give **expired air resuscitation (EAR)**.

● The air we *inhale* contains 20% oxygen and 0.4% carbon dioxide.

● The air we *exhale* contains 16% oxygen and 4% carbon dioxide.

How much we breathe

When we are resting, we breathe about 21 times per minute and take in about half a litre of air with each breath. When we exercise, we breathe more often and take in more air each time as more oxygen is required to give muscles energy. When we undertake vigorous exercise, we may breathe more deeply or pant, but there should be no wheezing or bubbling sounds as might be the case if you had a cold or influenza. Regular exercise increases our lung capacity and enables us to take in more oxygen with each breath.

Task 2

Devise a way to measure your breathing rate and then measure it. Then undertake a short fast exercise and record your breathing rate again. Compare your two scores with your partners.

Definitions

It is important to know certain definitions and two further ones to learn at this stage are for tidal volume and vital capacity.

tidal volume	the amount of air inspired and expired with each normal breath at rest or during exercise
vital capacity	the largest amount of air that can be made to pass into and out of the lungs by the most forceful inspiration and expiration (normally about 4–5 litres)

Task 3

Carry out the bell jar experiment shown here to measure your vital capacity.

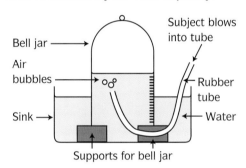

Equipment required:

- bell jar marked in 1 litre intervals
- large sink and access to water
- supports for bell jar to stand on
- rubber tube

Fill the bell jar and stand it on the supports. Take a deep breath (the largest inspiration), put your mouth around the rubber tube and exhale as much air as you can (most forceful expiration). Your vital capacity can be estimated by measuring how much water was expelled from the bell jar and replaced by the air you blew in.

Environmental hazards to health

Unfortunately the lungs are very delicate and they can easily lose their efficiency, even in a healthy person. They can be affected by air pollution from motor vehicles' exhaust fumes, industrial wastes and chemical insecticides.

People in certain occupations such as coal mining, may suffer from pneumoconiosis from inhaling coal dust.

The conditions inside the lungs are perfect for the growth of bacteria and also viruses such as colds and influenza, but the most obvious damage of all is caused by *smoking*.

Asthma affects the lungs, often making it difficult for the person to breathe. Some asthmatics use a Peak Flow metre which measures the elasticity of the lungs and may identify how well they can use the oxygen in the air.

Task 4

a Use a Peak Flow meter and record your scores over three attempts.

b In your exercise books, list the two main functions of the respiratory system.

c Explain the special nature of the capillaries in the circulatory system.

Key terms

- alveoli
- asthma
- capillaries
- gaseous exchange
- haemoglobin
- oxygen and carbon dioxide
- red blood cells
- tidal volume
- vital capacity

Immediate effects of exercise

When you exercise or take part in a strenuous sport you will notice several changes taking place in your body.

1 Your heart beats stronger and faster.
2 Your breathing quickens and deepens.
3 Your body temperature increases.
4 You start to sweat.
5 Your muscles begin to ache.

There is both a cause and a purpose for these physiological changes taking place.

1 Your heart beats stronger and faster

During exercise it is mainly **adrenaline** that produces changes in heartbeat and blood pressure. Adrenaline is a hormone which, when released, causes the heart rate to quicken. Its release can be caused by stressful situations.

It causes, amongst other things, glycogen to be released by the liver and blood to be diverted to the muscles and away from the organs (liver, kidney and brain). After eating a meal, more blood is sent to the digestive organs to help digest the food. This is one reason why you should not exercise after eating a large meal.

Some idea of fitness can be gained from the resting pulse rate, because an athlete's heart gets bigger and stronger than a non-athlete's, and it can supply the same amount of blood with fewer beats. So, the fitter you are, the lower your resting pulse rate, although other factors such as age, sex and body type also have an effect (see pages 68–71). However, the resting pulse rate does not tell the whole story because we need to know what happens during exercise and, just as important, how long the pulse rate takes to get back to normal. This is called the **recovery rate**.

Competitors in a marathon will experience all the immediate effects of exercise

2 Your breathing quickens and deepens

Breathing is greatly affected by exercise, because however fast the heart beats, it cannot carry enough oxygen if an insufficient supply is getting into the lungs. As well as how much air you can get into your lungs, the efficiency of breathing depends on how much oxygen can be removed from the air. The most important structures in oxygen uptake are the alveoli and, as we have seen, these can be impaired in a variety of ways.

Task 1

Write out three ways in which the alveoli can be affected or their function impaired.

Training can be of great benefit to the respiratory system. The capacity of the lungs is increased, which allows more air – and consequently more oxygen – to be taken in per breath, and carbon dioxide is removed more efficiently. More alveoli becomes available for gaseous exchange and oxygen uptake (VO_2 max.) is increased.

Overcoming problems

The problems produced by exercise or competition vary according to the type of event or sport in question. The problems for the sprinter are different from those of the middle distance runner. A short distance sprint may cause little problem to a trained sprinter, but a games player who has to repeatedly sprint needs to train to cope with this. The middle distance runner may not be running fast enough to get out of breath, but if they have to run up a steep hill, as in a cross-country race, they may get somewhat breathless. The same may be the case if they are required to produce a sprint at the end of, say, a 5000 metres race.

The problems for the marathon runner are quite unique. Here the emphasis is on stamina (endurance) rather than **power**, on economy rather than strength. It is not more oxygen that is needed, but stored up food. The problem may not lie in getting breathless, or supplying oxygen, but in having enough stored up glycogen (glucose) and fat in reserve to keep going.

Blood doping

While marathon runners try to store up glycogen (by carbo-loading – see page 50), some middle distance runners have tried to increase the oxygen-carrying capacity of the haemoglobin in the blood.

After a period of training carried out at high altitude (see also page 64), blood can be taken from the athlete, rather like from a blood donor, and stored. Just before a big race, e.g. the Olympic 5000 metres final, the blood is given back to the athlete. The athlete then has more blood to carry more oxygen, and as the blood was taken after altitude training, it is of very high quality in terms of oxygen uptake. This process, called blood doping, has now been made illegal (see Drugs in sport, pages 148–53).

Task 2

List three activities or times during an activity when you may become breathless.

Key terms

- adrenaline
- blood doping
- breathing
- heartbeat
- high altitude
- recovery rate

3 Your body temperature increases

When we exercise, our muscles are working and they generate heat, so our body temperature rises. The normal temperature in humans is 37°C (98.6°F) but temperatures between 36.4° and 37.2°C are accepted as within normal limits. Body temperature is regulated by heat radiating from the skin and water evaporating by sweating. When we shiver our muscles are working to produce heat in order to raise our body temperature.

4 You start to sweat

Not all the energy produced in **respiration** is used to produce muscle action. Some of this energy is turned into heat. As we have just seen, the body will tolerate a small rise in temperature, but very soon we begin to sweat. Sweat comes out of the pores of the skin, but when it reaches the surface it evaporates. In order for it to evaporate, energy (in the form of heat) is needed, and this heat comes from the body. As we lose heat, our body temperature will fall and it is this latent heat loss that cools the body. However, when we sweat we also loose salt as well as water and this can cause problems.

Barry McGuigan lost his world boxing championship in the sweltering heat of Las Vegas

> ## Task 3
>
> List three sports in which drinks are taken at regular intervals.

Controlling water loss

Under normal conditions our body's water content is controlled.

> amount of water in = amount of water out
>
> (food and drink in = urine and sweat out)

If the conditions are hot, we sweat more and produce less urine but, unlike panting dogs, we lose salt as well as body heat and water. We have to replace the salt so that the body stays the same, otherwise we will get **cramp.**

So we need:

water + salt

or we may faint or collapse. In certain sports this is not uncommon – boxing is a good example, when fights take place in high temperatures and go on for a long time. We now see drinks being taken during football, tennis, cycling and many other games that go on for a long time, in which competitors can sweat a lot and which take place in high temperatures.

However, we can return to the marathon for the clearest example of a sport that requires almost superhuman exertion over a long period of time, often in high temperatures. Approved refreshments are supplied at regular feeding stations along the marathon route. The sugar solutions that are provided, either by the organizers or by the athletes themselves, mean that used energy, in the form of glucose, can be replaced along with the water or liquids required to prevent **dehydration** (drying out) and cramp. It is for this reason that refreshments must be taken both before and during the early stages of the race.

Cramp often strikes at the end of a long, hard game

5 Your muscles begin to ache!

As we now know, in order to work, muscles need energy. Energy comes from food, which is mainly converted to glucose (sugar). To work most efficiently muscles also need plenty of oxygen. Glucose and oxygen are brought to the muscles in the blood. Wastes such as carbon dioxide are carried away in the blood. This process of getting energy is called respiration. The equation used to describe respiration is:

$$Glucose + oxygen \rightarrow engery + Co_2 + water$$

When muscles do extra work more glucose and oxygen are needed, so more blood must flow to the muscles, so the heart beats faster. Now the blood vessels will narrow to raise the pressure, so more blood is sent to the muscles instead of to the organs of the body. Eventually it becomes impossible to get enough oxygen to the muscles so they use a different method of getting energy. Glucose is still used, but now there is a waste product called **lactic acid.**

Lactic acid is a poison. After a while it will make the muscle ache and eventually it will cause cramp, and the muscles will stop working. The athlete has to rest while the blood brings fresh supplies of oxygen to the muscles.

Aerobic and anaerobic respiration

- Production of energy *with* oxygen is called **aerobic respiration.**
- Production of energy *without* oxygen is called **anaerobic respiration.**

The build-up of lactic acid is slow during exercise at up to 75% of maximum work rate, but when we work at a higher work rate it builds up in the muscles much more quickly. This can be due to poor training, which is the main reason, or by the depletion of glycogen stores in the muscles as a result of massive muscular effort. Examples of the latter situation would be a marathon race, or a hard football match played in muddy conditions which has gone to extra time.

Task 4

Write down the two fuels that are required to give energy to muscles.

Key terms

- **aerobic respiration**
- **anaerobic respiration**
- **body temperature**
- **cramp**
- **lactic acid**
- **sweat**

Effects of regular training and exercise

- The heart pumps more blood per beat.
- The recovery rate becomes quicker.
- The resting pulse rate becomes lower.
- The number of capillaries increases.
- The **cardiovascular** system becomes more efficient.

Task 1

Copy and complete the following sentences.

a _____ _____ is the amount of blood pumped with each beat of the heart. With training this increases. Therefore this increase is a short-term effect of exercise.

b The _____ _____ _____ is the heart rate at rest. There is much variation, but it is normally between 60–80 b.p.m. A person who exercises regularly, even over a short period of time, may reduce their RPR and this reduction is therefore a short-term effect of exercise.

Some idea of fitness can be gained from the resting pulse rate (RPR), because with training our heart gets bigger and stronger, and it can supply the same amount of blood with fewer beats. However, the RPR does not tell the whole story because it is just as important to know how long the pulse rate takes to get back to normal (i.e. our recovery rate). The quicker this happens the fitter we are.

With increasing fitness, the number of capillaries within the muscles increases. This would reduce the damage caused in the event of a heart attack (see page 62).

Task 2

a Copy and complete the following sentence.

The amount of blood pumped by the heart in one minute is called the

_____ _____.

b Take the answers to tasks **1a**, **1b** and **2a** and write out the formula that connects them together.

Key terms

- **heart rate**
- **recovery rate**
- **effects of exercise**

Everyone can benefit from the short-term effects of exercise

Long-term benefits of exercise

- It reduces the risk of coronary heart disease (CHD).
- You can work harder for longer.

Exercise reduces the risk of coronary heart disease (CHD) in a number of ways. It obviously improves the cardiovascular system and helps to reduce blood pressure. In the earlier units we learned that it helps to reduce stress and burns off excess calories. If we are keen to get fit this will probably motivate us not to smoke. Smoking is the biggest cause of CHD. So this is a longer-term effect of exercise.

The heart

Over a period of time we can see that the heart of a fit person will beat far fewer times. This makes it much more efficient and causes less stress to be put on the heart. This is a long-term effect of exercise.

With training, the heart muscle increases in size, thickness and strength, the chambers increase in volume and so the whole heart gets bigger, therefore we can work harder for longer, This is another long-term effect of exercise.

Tasks

a   Write out in your own words what is meant by cardiovascular fitness.

b   Suggest three ways in which you can improve cardiovascular fitness.

Causes and repercussions of CHD

Heart disease causes more deaths in the developed world than any other disease. Most of the deaths caused by smoking are through heart attacks – not cancer, as many people believe. However, there are other reasons why people die from heart disease and these include hereditary conditions, infections, narrowing of the coronary arteries and high blood pressure.

The most common form of heart disease in Britain is atherosclerosis, which is caused by deposits of fat and cholesterol on the inside walls of the coronary arteries. People who suffer from this condition are often short of breath, especially after exercise, and suffer chest pains called angina. This condition causes an increase in blood pressure, as a result of the narrowing of the arteries. The flow of blood is therefore impeded, in much the same way as if you were to pinch the end of a garden hosepipe when the water is flowing through it. This situation can lead to a heart attack.

Some contributory causes of coronary heart disease are:

- high cholesterol due to a poor diet which may be high in animal fats
- sedentary living
- lack of exercise
- stress
- smoking.

Key terms

- **angina**
- **atherosclerosis**
- **cardiovascular system**
- **coronary heart disease (CHD)**
- **long-term effects**

Aerobic and anaerobic activity

Aerobic activity

On pages 34–7 we looked at the factors that would help to make a sports champion. We discovered that there are many natural assets, but that the importance of each varies according to the sport in question. We then looked in some depth into the importance of body composition and found that a person's somatotype (pages 52–7) could have an influence on their performance in sport. This can be affected by many things, such as diet and nutrition, percentage body fat, and lean body mass.

Cardiovascular fitness (pages 58–9) is also a factor, but like body composition it can be influenced and developed to a high degree. However, the level to which it is developed depends again on the sport in question. Cardiovascular fitness is sometimes called **aerobic** fitness, and it is also often referred to as cardiovascular endurance.

Jogging is a popular aerobic activity

Definitions

cardiovascular fitness	the fitness of the heart, blood and blood vessels
aerobic (or *with air*) fitness	the ability to exercise or compete, for a long time, at a level that allows the respiratory system to cope physiologically (i.e. without getting breathless or getting cramp)

Aerobics

Aerobic activities, or aerobics, became popular over 20 years ago, with classes for both women and men taking place in many sports centres, schools and village halls. It has now grown into a massive industry with many famous people being linked with videos, books and television programmes. It has broadened out into, for example, step aerobics and swim/aqua aerobics and appeals to both men and women of all ages. There are, as we shall see, many other ways to improve aerobic fitness. The most common would be continuous training, but other ways would include:

- interval training (see page 94)
- fartlek training (see page 96)
- circuit training (see page 97).

Task 1

Find the names of a book, a video and a television programme that are about aerobics or any other type of aerobic activity.

Anaerobic activity

Definitions

anaerobic (or *without air*) fitness	the ability to work at a high intensity for a short period of time and then to repay your respiratory system *after* completing the training session or competition

Brisk walking is now recognized as being one of the best ways to exercise for aerobic or cardiovascular fitness, and, like jogging using a treadmill, reduces the risk of joint injuries

Anaerobic exercise can only last for about 40 seconds or so, about the time it takes a world class 400 metres runner to complete the race. Even the highest class and fittest of performers cannot work at this intensity for any longer. The repayment comes in the form of deep gasping breaths at the end of the activity. This is to enable as much oxygen as possible to get back into the respiratory system, and to eliminate as much of the waste product as possible, mostly in the form of carbon dioxide. Repayment in this way is known as **oxygen debt**, the debt being the amount consumed in recovery above what would normally be consumed at rest in the same time.

Cross-training

Another method of aerobic training that is now becoming popular is known as cross-training. This is when more than one activity is undertaken to add variety to the programme and to equal out the workout in terms of muscles used. For example, in a 40-minute session you might spend 20 minutes jogging and 20 minutes on a rowing machine.

Task 2

Think of two other activities that would compliment each other in this way.

Task 3

Think of three games in which the performer works at their maximum or near maximum for about 40 seconds.

Key terms

- **anaerobic fitness**
- **body composition**
- **carbon dioxide**
- **cardiovascular or aerobic fitness**
- **oxygen debt**

Aerobic ←			→ Anaerobic
● marathon	● distance running ● distance swimming ● distance cycling ● distance canoeing ● midfield players	● football ● hockey ● rugby ● netball ● 1500 m running ● 800 m running	● sprinting ● sprint swimming ● sprint cycling ● sprinting in games ● 400 m running

Aerobic/anaerobic combinations

Different sports require varying amounts of aerobic or anaerobic fitness. The table above shows how the aerobic/anaerobic needs of different sports change gradually through these activities.

It is very important to remember that cardiovascular fitness is not just for the top sportspeople. It is the most important aspect of fitness for all of us because it involves the circulatory and the respiratory systems.

Task 4

a Explain, from a game of your choice, when and how aerobic and anaerobic activity might be involved.

b Explain in your own words the difference between aerobic and anaerobic activity.

The heart or cardiac muscle is different from any other muscle in the body in that it *never tires*. It must continually pump blood, without which we would die. If the blood vessels become blocked or hardened, angina or a heart attack occurs.

Improved cardiovascular fitness increases the number of blood vessels around the heart, so lessening the risk of a heart attack.

Task 5

Compare, from a game of your choice, the different requirements for aerobic and anaerobic fitness needed for players of different positions in this game – e.g. for a goalkeeper or centre forward in football.

Key terms

● **cardiac muscle**
● **circulatory system**
● **respiratory system**

Squash requires a combination of aerobic and anaerobic fitness

The principles of training

There are different ways in which we can improve cardiovascular fitness, and there are certain principles of training which need to be understood.

Systematic training for individual needs

It is important that the training programme should be systematic, or planned, and it should also be devised to fit individual needs. If a person likes swimming and they are set a jogging programme which they dislike, the chances of them successfully getting fit and staying fit are minimal. In other words, do not use someone else's programme.

Likewise, training programmes for marathon runners may vary because individuals have different needs One runner may have more time, another more motivation. Another example might be a rugby centre, who would have different training needs from a prop or a hooker.

Task 1

Other than rugby, think of a sport where two people who take part have different training needs.

Specificity

This means that if you wish to develop a certain aspect of training, say cardiovascular fitness, then you emphasize that aspect in your programme. For example, if the sport for which you are training is squash, your training would be quite different from someone who is training for the London Marathon.

Task 2

Write down three different sports which have similar fitness needs. Mention specific positions if this is relevant.

Key terms

- individual needs
- specificity
- systematic

Olympic swimmers train for specific events and swimmers spend a lot of time actually in the water. They need to develop cardiovascular fitness but they *swim* to achieve this – they do not go jogging!

Specific training

The need for specific training within a sport can be seen very easily in activities such as rugby where the backs and the forwards need different training/fitness. Similarly, in football and hockey, the goalkeepers need different training/fitness from the outfield players. In fact, professional clubs actually have different trainers and coaches for goalkeepers.

Overload

Another training principle is that of **overload** – often mistaken for meaning *too much!* This is not what it means. Overload means training in a worthwhile range of intensity above the minimum amount required to improve fitness,

known as the minimum threshold of training, and below the maximum threshold of training. The area in between these two thresholds is known as the target range or target zone. We saw how to work out the target range for cardiovascular fitness on page 71. Top sportspeople need to work at a higher rate in order to reach their maximal potential.

The principle of overload is true for all areas of health-related exercise. For example, in muscular strength, where the weight lifted for a particular programme may be between 60 per cent to 80 per cent of maximum effort, or in muscular endurance where it may be that the number of repetitions is between 60 per cent to 80 per cent of maximum repetitions (see page 94).

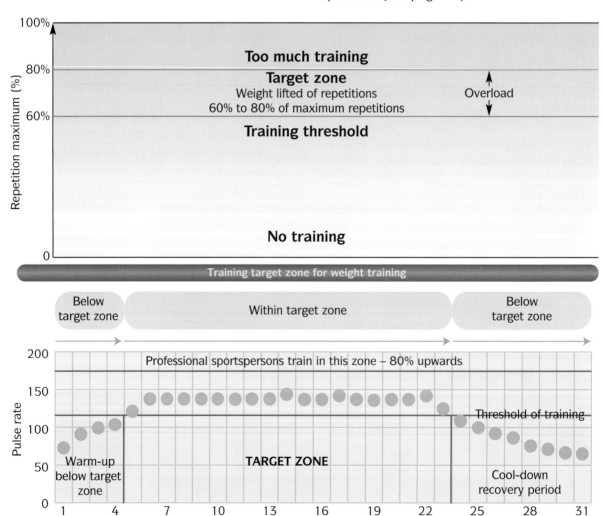

FITT principle

This leads into the **FITT** principle. This is a mnemonic (an aid to memory) which will help you to remember the different parts of the principle.

F   is for *frequency*

I   is for *intensity*

T   is for *time*

T   is for *type*

Frequency

F is for frequency, or how many times per week you need to train in order to improve your fitness. A minimum of three times a week is recommended. However, if you wanted to run a marathon, become an Olympic athlete or a professional at your sport, it is unlikely that you could achieve this on three training sessions a week.

Intensity

I is for intensity, or how hard you train. As we have seen in relation to cardiovascular fitness, in order to improve you must train at an intensity that will take your pulse into the target range.

Time

T is for time, or how long each session must be in order to be of any benefit and to achieve improvement. The amount must be at least 20 minutes per session in the target range, not 5 minutes to change, 5 minutes to train, 5 minutes to shower and 5 minutes to change back again! In terms of cardiovascular fitness, it means 20 minutes minimum with the pulse in the target range, after a **warm-up** and followed by a **cool-down.** Again, top sportspeople have to train for much longer to reach the levels of fitness they require. Top athletes will spend more than 20 minutes warming up, and a marathon runner will spend about 2 hours running 20 miles each Sunday, apart from all the other training they do during the week.

Type

T is for type, or what sort of training you do. For most people, this could be a wide variety of activities, as long as it will raise the pulse rate into the target zone and keep it there for at least 20 minutes. It could vary from disco dancing to swimming, or it could include cycling, brisk walking, jogging or aerobics. It also does not matter whether the type of activity is aerobic or anaerobic, however it *would* if you were a sportsperson who specialized in one type of activity.

Task 2

Write down three ways you can think of to increase the intensity of a training session.

Regularity and moderation

Most benefit is gained from training on a regular basis, so regularity of training is similar to the F for Frequency of training in the FITT principle. Recent research suggests that 30 minutes of exercise five times a week is a realistic measure for achieving optimal fitness. If you train for 30 minutes four times each week, you will have trained twice as much as the recommended minimum of three times for 20 minutes in the FITT principle. This leads us onto another term – moderation, which means getting the balance right between not training enough and training too much or over training. Achieving this balance is very important.

Key terms

- cool-down
- FITT principle
- frequency
- intensity
- moderation
- overload
- regularity
- target zone
- time
- type
- warm-up

Progression

Having planned a training programme and followed it over a period of, say, six weeks, the athlete would need to re-test and evaluate their fitness levels, to check for improvements or otherwise. This then brings us to the principle of **progression**. This involves further planning to produce another programme which would take the athlete on to a higher level programme, perhaps training more often (frequency), perhaps more strenuously (intensity), or spending longer (time) or a combination of such factors. So progression means to gradually increase your training programme.

Reversibility

If training progressively gradually improves fitness over a long period of time, what happens if less training takes place, or if the training sessions are made easier?

This brings us to the final principle of training called **reversibility**. This means that instead of progressing or remaining at the same level, the athlete gradually loses fitness. This sometimes happens when a sportsperson is injured for a long time, or even more so if they become seriously ill. Some people seem to be able to keep their fitness a little longer than others, but everyone will lose fitness if they stop training.

Task 3

One way to measure both progression and reversibility is to take your pulse rate after completing your training programme, and then measure how long it takes for your pulse rate to get back to normal. Look at the chart below. How long did it take for this person's pulse rate to recover?

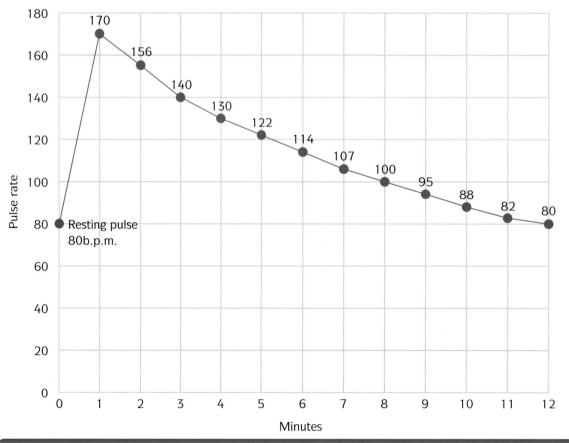

One person's recovery rate after one minute of strenuous exercise

The 9 principles of training

The 9 principles of training, as we have seen in this unit, are therefore:

1   individual needs
2   systematic programming
3   overload
4   specificity
5   progression
6   FITT
7   regularity
8   moderation
9   reversibility.

Although these principles are set out here in order to show how they apply to cardiovascular fitness, the same principles apply to all other aspects of fitness and health-related exercise.

Task 4

a   Write out two lists, one headed 'London Marathon winner' and one headed 'London Marathon fun runner'. Below these titles give the reasons why each would have taken part in the race.

b   Explain in a short paragraph, and using the information above, how the fun runner's training for this race would have differed from that of the elite athlete.

Key terms

● evaluate
● FITT
● individual needs
● overload
● progression
● reversibility
● specificity
● systematic
● training needs

The training needs of this London Marathon 'fun runner' (top) would have been quite different from those of Catherina McKiernan (bottom), winner of the women's race. They would have spent a very different amount of time training. The distances would also have been different, as would the intensity of the running. They would have different expectations from the outcome, but in his own way, the fun runner would have achieved as much, have worked as hard and got his deserved reward for his efforts

Warm-up, main activity and cool-down

The warm-up

A **warm-up** gradually raises body temperature and heart rate, and improves the exchange of oxygen from haemoglobin (see page 74).

Even on warm summer days, or if indoors, performers usually wear warm clothing during the warm-up, usually a tracksuit or jogging bottoms and a sweater. At the conclusion of the main activity, they put on their warm clothing before cooling down.

We warm up for three reasons:

1   to prevent injury
2   to improve performance
3   to prepare psychologically for the event.

A warm-up should provide a smooth transition from rest to the intensity of the main activity or competitive situation.

> ### Task 1
>
> Explain the connection between oxygen and haemoglobin.

Cardiovascular warm-up

Every training/exercise session or competitive situation, should start with a cardiovascular warm-up, which raises the pulse rate gradually towards the working pulse rate. This can take various forms and could include easy cycling on an exercise bike, with little or no resistance, skipping, slow swimming, easy jogging or walking. This part of the warm-up usually takes between five and ten minutes, depending on the athlete and the event. International athletes would probably take much longer.

Stretching

Stretching forms the second phase of the warm-up, and there are three ways to do this.

1   **Static** – easy stretches which are held for about 10–15 seconds, without straining.
2   **Ballistic** – bouncing stretches (which are not recommended).
3   **Proprioceptive neuromuscular facilitation (PNF)** – these are assisted stretches using the help of the coach/ teacher or training partner.

> ### Task 2
>
> Name a sport of your choice and then describe three stretches that you might use in your warm-up. They should be:
>
> ● suitable for the sport
> ● for different parts of the body
> ● static stretches.

A warm-up on a treadmill is easy to control

Static stretches are recommended as a part of a warm-up routine

Static stretching

Static stretching is recommended and it should be related to the main activity. For example, if the game is football then stretching the gastrocnemius, hamstring and quadriceps is essential, but the goalkeeper would need to include some specialist exercises, perhaps of a gymnastics nature. A swimmer would include stretches that would be specific to the stroke or strokes that they are about to compete in, and would no doubt include a variety, from neck and shoulder stretches to ankle stretches.

Normally stretching starts at the top (e.g. neck and shoulder stretches) and works down to the feet and ankles, as suggested for the swimmer.

Ballistic stretching

Although ballistic stretching is not recommended, you may see some top athletes doing this type of stretching just before an event. However, this is more likely to be part of their preparation ritual than their warm-up. In any case they will probably have been warming up for a very long time (using static stretching) by this stage.

Finishing the warm-up

The warm-up should be timed to finish just before the main activity or event starts. For games players, it would be finished off with some fast sprints over short distances.

Another example would be the hurdlers who sprint over the first few hurdles. The first sprint should not take place during the game.

Key terms

- **ballistic**
- **cardiovascular**
- **PNF stretching**
- **static**
- **warm-up**

The main activity

The main activity may take a variety of forms. It may vary in terms of training sessions (e.g. **interval training**, **continuous training**, **fartlek**, **circuit training** or **weight training**, all of which will be covered later), according to the performer. For example, why are they training: to lose weight, to win a world title, as part of their rehabilitation after injury or illness, or to improve their current fitness state?

The main activity may also vary according to the performer's body build (somatotype), the level of performer (e.g. elite athlete or fun runner) and whether they are a professional sportsperson or an amateur. Other factors include the time of year (e.g. pre-season, competition/taper period) and the type of session (e.g. cardiovascular fitness, aerobic/anaerobic, muscular strength, muscular endurance, to help lose weight or to improve **flexibility**).

It may be a skill session or a combination of fitness and skill, or it may be the actual performance – for example, a football match, a tennis match or a dance performance.

If the main activity includes both skill and fitness sessions, this may cause a difficulty in terms of which comes first, the skill session or the fitness session. If the skill session comes first, then the performer may not be able to perform well in the fitness aspect, but if the fitness comes first, the performer may not be able to perform well in the skill aspect.

Sometimes the sessions can be combined, incorporating skill with the training, but quite often the training comes first with the skill coming last, finishing with the game situation.

Task 3

Name your sport and then name a skill or situation that you want to improve. Then devise a practice drill that could be used to improve the skill or situation.

An example is given below.

Sport: football Aim: to improve passing ability under pressure
Xs outside the square have a ball each and try to pass the ball to the Xs inside the square.
Xs inside the square make one touch to return the ball to the same X, who can change their position outside the square. Os try to intercept the pass.

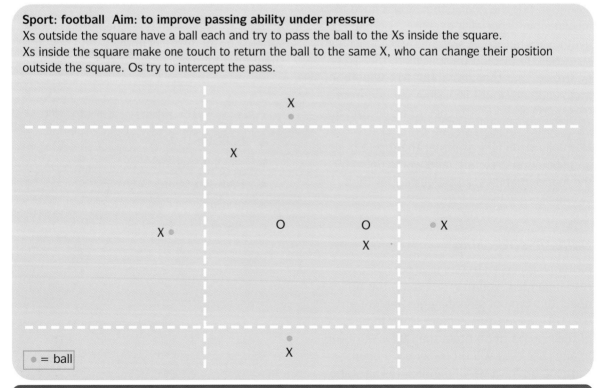

= ball

Drill to improve passing under pressure

Lesson 24: Warm-up, main activity and cool-down

The cool-down

The **cool-down** gradually returns the body to its normal temperature and the working pulse rate to the resting pulse rate. It helps to prevent stiffness and soreness in the muscles by dispersing lactic acid (see page 79).

Every training session or participation in physical activity, either competitive or non-competitive, should finish with a cool-down. It is most important after anaerobic activity. The performer or competitor will normally put back on the warm clothing they used to warm up in. In order to return the pulse to its previous rate, a similar activity could be used as the one to warm-up (e.g. exercise bicycle, jogging, etc.). This type of activity also helps to prevent blood pooling in the lower limbs, by assisting the return of venous blood to the heart.

The cool-down takes between ten and fifteen minutes, five minutes to return the pulse to normal and ten minutes of static stretching to disperse lactic acid.

Static stretches in the cool-down are held for longer than in the warm-up, about 30–35 seconds is usual. The stretches should again reflect the activity. For example, as in the warm-up, a footballer would make sure they stretched the muscles in the legs. If the performer has been circuit training using a variety of muscles, then all of these muscles should be re-stretched in the cool-down.

As in the warm-up, the stretches should be done in sequence, starting at the top and gradually working down through the body.

Relaxation exercises

Ideally, the session should finish with some relaxation exercises, especially if the main activity has been very hard and/or anaerobic in nature. This will last about two or three minutes and could take the form of lying down on one's back and tensing and relaxing specific muscle groups for ten seconds. Once again starting at the top and working down. Finish with 20 seconds lying with eyes shut, feeling heavy – imagine you are on a beach, warm and feeling heavy. Then stand up slowly and return to the changing rooms.

This helps to relieve stress, and after showering and changing, leads to a feeling of well being, a main aim of fitness training for many people.

Contra-indicated exercises

Some exercises are likely to cause injury and should be avoided (see pages 132–3).

Relaxation exercises are a good way to finish the cool-down

Task 4

Explain how lactic acid is produced and describe what might be the consequences if it isn't dispersed.

Key terms

- blood pooling
- contra-indicated exercises
- cool-down
- main activity
- practice drill
- relaxation exercises

Methods of training

Relays and shuttle runs are a form of interval training

Interval training

Interval training is used in many different sports, from individual activities such as swimming and athletics to games such as football and hockey. Athletes may train individually, with a partner or in a team or group, but whichever they choose to do, they will have periods of work followed by periods of rest.

The work interval may be a distance to run, say 60 metres, or a time to run, say 10 seconds.

The rest interval may be a walk back to the starting mark, or simply not working (rest). This should be at least 30 seconds in duration in order to allow recovery, ready for the next work interval, otherwise the quality of work, or the intensity, will not be good enough. The aim is for a quality workout!

A repetition may be 1 run of 60 metres. A set (of repetitions) may be 4 repetitions. In swimming it may be a 25 metre length, again

in sets of 4 repetitions. The rest period will be 30 seconds. In a training session for a game, you might expect to run a 20 metre sprint and then rest while 3 or 4 others in your team run 20 metres (your rest time), then you repeat your run. You may repeat this 4 times.

An athlete may perform a number of sets of repetitions, say 4, with longer rest intervals between sets. For example, 4 sets of 4 × 60 metres with a walk back between repetitions and 3 minutes between sets.

Advantages of interval training

- It includes repeated sprint running or swimming, which is anaerobic.
- It takes place over short periods or bursts.
- It includes a rest period (interval) which allows for recovery.
- It includes repetitions of high quality, which raises the pulse to near maximal.

Continuous training

Continuous training may be the most appropriate training to improve cardiovascular endurance for a sedentary adult who has not trained for some time, and is quite unfit. The training may take various forms and could start with brisk walking and graduate to jogging. It could be over a distance, say one mile, or a time, say ten minutes.

Interval training may be more suitable for team game players, as it fits the style of many games, with short bursts followed by slow walking or jogging or stopping, but continuous training may be more appropriate at the start of a season, or during the off-season. Long-distance athletes may use continuous training or, more likely, a combination of both interval, continuous and fartlek (see page 96). For example, one week's training for a good marathon runner may be:

Task 1

a On your own or with a partner of about the same fitness, walk briskly for fifteen minutes. Check your starting and finishing points. How far do you think you have walked?

This may be a good way to start training after injury or after a long lay-off.

b On your own or with the same partner, start from the same point and try to jog continuously for seven minutes over the same course. How close are you to the finishing point of your walk? How far do you think you have run?

Which session did you find the hardest?

Day	a.m.	p.m.
Monday	5 miles easy	8 miles brisk
Tuesday	6 miles fartlek – several 1 minute bursts	
Wednesday	5 miles easy	10 miles with 6 × 2 minute hill runs
Thursday	8 miles continuous run	
Friday	5 miles easy	5 miles jog
Saturday	rest	
Sunday	20–22 miles continuous run	

Advantages of continuous training

- Apart from good footwear in the case of running, it is very cheap.
- You can work on your own or with a group.
- It is suitable for health and fitness.
- It improves aerobic fitness.
- It can take place in a variety of places.
- It can be adapted to suite individual needs.

Key terms

- **continuous training**
- **individual needs**
- **interval training**
- **repetitions**
- **rest interval**
- **set**
- **work interval**

Fartlek running

Fartlek running originated in Sweden – the word fartlek means 'speedplay' in Swedish. It came about before interval training and is a combination of fast and slow running. In Scandinavia it was originally carried out in the countryside in pleasant terrain and often included running up hills.

In many ways fartlek running resembles interval training. During a fartlek session, sprints of varying distances will be included, but not necessarily over a measured distance, perhaps from one tree to another, or up a hill of no measured distance. So you have sprints and jogs, or periods of work followed by periods of rest.

Advantages of fartlek running

- It can be done in a variety of terrain (e.g. sand dunes, parkland or forest).
- It can include hill work, both uphill and downhill.
- It can include repetitions and programmes are very flexible.
- Rest periods can be included or the session can be continuous with intermittent hard and easy running.

Cross training

Cross training is a mixture of training often used to break up the monotony of a single type of training. It can also help to reduce stresses on the body from a single training regime, for example, running on hard surfaces every day gives a continual pounding to the joints of the lower body. Cross training can be used to produce the same effects as a single type of training, but through using quite different types of work/play. Because it is a mixture of different types of training, it can be adapted to suit an individual's needs, for example, one day swimming, one day running, one day playing squash. This type of training might not suit the top athletes, but it is a very good way to keep a high level of general fitness for the average person.

Advantages of cross training

- It allows for variety in training and can therefore make training more interesting.
- You can train with different people in different activities, or alone.
- Certain muscle groups can be rested from day to day. Road running one day, cycling another, swimming another would develop different muscle groups.
- Training can be adapted to weather conditions – indoor squash substituted for running if weather was bad.

Task 2

Write a short paragraph to compare interval training, continuous training, fartlek running and cross training.

Circuit training

The aim of **circuit training** is to improve local muscular endurance, cardiovascular fitness and circulo-respiratory fitness (i.e. the heart, blood, blood vessels and the lungs). Circuit training involves a number of exercises, set out so that you avoid exercising the same muscle group consecutively. Each exercise takes place at a 'station', in a gymnasium, sports hall, or outside.

Repetitions

Exercises may by carried out for a length of time, e.g. 15–30 seconds, or a set number of times, according to fitness level. After completing each set of repetitions, the athlete moves on to the next exercise, until a whole circuit of exercises is complete. The athlete may then rest, say for three minutes, before repeating the circuit. Some circuit training sessions are quite sophisticated, perhaps using a different number of repetitions for different levels of fitness, or they may use colour-coded cards for each level of performer. Exercises may be done to music, which will stop every 30 seconds and restart after another 10. That's 30 seconds of work time and 10 seconds of rest time.

Extra exercises may also be added or the rest period shortened to make the circuit harder, or to increase the intensity.

Circuit training is currently very popular and many exercise classes now include this type of work in the session.

Another way to use a circuit is to have a skills circuit for a particular sport. In this case, instead of doing different exercises at each station, a different skill from a sport can be practised. For example, a basketball skills circuit could have dribbling at station 1, then chest passes at station 2, then shooting at station 3, etc.

Advantages of circuit training

There are many advantages to circuit training.

- It offers a much more general all round fitness than the other three methods (and also weight training – see page 102).
- It includes strength, endurance, power, flexibility and speed.
- The equipment need not be expensive.
- People of all levels of fitness and ability can take part as exercises can be tailored to suit individual needs.
- It includes both aerobic and anaerobic activities.
- It uses a wide range of exercises.
- People work hard and can be highly motivated to succeed.
- It uses the overload principle of training.

Task 3

Think of any training session you have been involved in and then write out what sport or activity it was and what you did. Then state which of these four types of training session – interval, fartlek, cross, or circuit training – you think it was.

Hygiene

Whatever methods of training you use, remember that hygiene is important while taking part in sport. There is a strong link between hygiene and health. Always make a complete change into appropriate clothing and footwear for your sports activity. Two areas related to hygiene you need to know about and remember are athlete's foot and verrucae.

Athlete's foot

This is an infection of the skin caused by a fungus. It causes dry, flaky skin and itching between the toes. It is easily transmitted by sharing towels or socks, or from wet floors in a changing room or a swimming pool. Pools usually have a special footbath for swimmers to use to help prevent infection. Athlete's foot can be prevented by frequently changing socks and by using a fresh pair when taking part in exercise, not wearing sweaty training shoes and by applying plenty of foot powder. Special powders to treat athlete's foot are available from chemists.

Verrucae

Verrucae (or plantar warts) are caused by a viral infection and normally appear on the sole of the foot, often singly. They can make walking very painful. Like athlete's foot, they can be passed on in swimming pools and from the wet floors. A special sock can be worn to prevent passing on this infection. Verrucae can be treated in a number of ways – removed in a small operation, or by applying liquid nitrogen to them.

Key terms

- athlete's foot
- cardiovascular fitness
- circuit training
- circulo-respiratory fitness
- fartlek running
- hill work
- intensity
- repetitions
- verrucae

Comparing two types of training session

A group of athletes might work on a training session in this way.

Each member of the group would have a training partner to help to take their pulse counts.

After a suitable warm-up the main activity for the training session might be:

Session A

No. 1s   Using a rolling start:
1   Run 60 metres at 90% effort.
2   Walk back slowly to allow recovery.
3   Repeat (1) and (2) a further five times.
4   After the sixth repetition take the pulse rate for fifteen seconds and multiply this figure by four.
5   Allowing one-minute intervals between pulse counts take ten pulse counts in all.
6   Complete a suitable cool-down.

No. 2s   Complete the same session and record pulse counts.

Task 1

Work in pairs (i.e. one person will be No. 1, the other No. 2). Carry out a similar training session. When it is not your turn to train, you should help your partner by taking and recording their pulse counts. Remember to record ten pulse counts.

Homework

Plot your pulse counts on the graph on Worksheet 25 (page 154) of the Teacher's Resource File and mark your target zone on it (see page 71).

Session B

No. 1s   Using a standing start on a 400 metre track:
1   Run 600 metres at 75% effort.
2   Walk back slowly to the start to allow recovery.
3   Repeat (1) and (2) a further three times.
4   After the fourth repetition take the pulse rate for fifteen seconds and multiply this figure by four.
5   Allowing one-minute intervals between pulse counts take ten pulse counts in all.
6   Complete a suitable cool-down.

No. 2s   Complete the same session and record pulse counts.

Task 2

Carry out session B with a partner. Take and record your pulse counts as before. Remember to record ten pulse counts.

Homework

Plot the pulse counts on the graph and mark your target zone on it.

Anaerobic and aerobic fitness

Both of these sessions would improve cardiovascular fitness but in different ways. Session A is anaerobic, suitable for a 100 metres runner, while session B is more suited to aerobic fitness, such as that needed for a 1500 metres runner.

Points to learn from this exercise

- Session A is very short distance work and from a rolling start the athletes will run at a very fast pace, thereby improving their speed and fitness.
- Each of these sessions uses the principle of **specificity.**
- The pulse rate taken at the end of each run is called the working pulse.
- This type of training has periods of work followed by periods of rest and is called interval training.

The rest allows the athlete to recover, to pay back the oxygen debt and/or deal with the build up of lactic acid in the muscle. The work done can therefore be of a higher intensity and so build up the athlete's endurance.

Personal exercise programme (PEP)

These are the methods from which you can plan for your personal exercise programme (PEP), in order to improve your cardiovascular fitness.

Pages 94–9 should help you to understand what types of training are available to you, and how they affect your cardiovascular and respiratory systems. The training sessions set out opposite are difficult ones and at first you may not be able to cope with them. In this case simply make them easier, either by doing less, or by doing them at a lower intensity.

Task 4

Write down what your favourite sport is. Then, from the methods of training described on pages 94–9, choose the one you like best and explain why.

Key terms

- cool-down
- interval training
- lactic acid
- oxygen debt
- specificity
- target zone
- warm-up

Task 3

Work out from the chart on the right how many minutes it took for this person's working pulse rate to return to the resting pulse rate. Check this result against the one on page 88. If this was the same athlete, what can you note from this second result? Which training principle is operating?

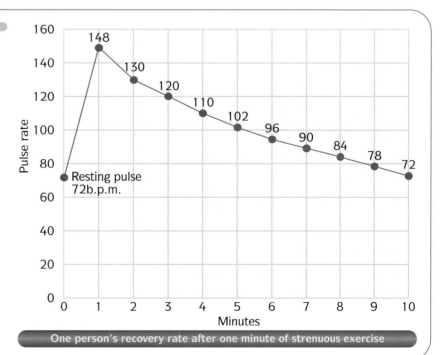

One person's recovery rate after one minute of strenuous exercise

Muscular strength and muscular endurance

This unit looks at muscular strength and muscular endurance, the importance of each in sport, health and exercise, and how to develop them for each of these aspects. But first there are some definitions to learn.

Definitions

muscular strength	the ability of the muscles to exert force. Weight lifting is a good example of this, when you lift the heaviest weight you can manage – in one go! Charles Corbin, an American health-related exercise expert, describes it as 'the amount of force you can produce with a single maximum effort'
muscular endurance	the ability to use the voluntary muscles many times without getting tired

Source: Edexcel specification

Weight lifters demonstrate enormous muscular strength

We need muscular strength in our everyday life for some if not all of the following reasons.

1 to increase work capacity
2 to decrease the chance of injury
3 to prevent lower back pain
4 to improve or prevent poor posture
5 to improve athletic performance
6 to save a life or property in an emergency situation
7 to aid rehabilitation after illness or injury

Task

In your exercise books, write out a list of reasons for needing strength.

Improving muscular strength

Muscular strength is gained by using heavy weights and few repetitions. Overload (see page 86) is used in the amount of weight or resistance, often using the pyramid system of training. An example of this system for a bench (chest) press of 60kg could be:

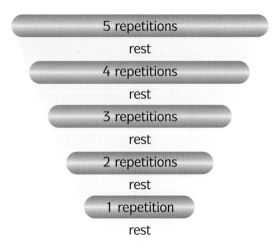

5 repetitions
rest
4 repetitions
rest
3 repetitions
rest
2 repetitions
rest
1 repetition
rest

If you can lift more than one single repetition at the end then the starting weight was too low!

Many people use muscular endurance as a part of their everyday life

Improving muscular endurance

Circuit training is a good example of how to improve muscular endurance. Another example is the sets method of weight training, where lighter resistance is used but a higher number of repetitions are carried out. For example: bench (chest) press, 3 sets of 10 repetitions using 20 kg resistance.

Repetitions and sets

These form the basis of training to improve both muscular strength and endurance:

● A repetition is one exercise of a particular movement, e.g. a bench press.

● A set is a number of repetitions of a particular exercise, e.g. 10 repetitions of the bench press.

In a schedule or programme you might do 3 sets of each exercise, e.g. 3 sets of 10 bench presses using 20 kg, with a rest of 3 minutes between sets. So overload is achieved by using a high number of repetitions.

Measuring strength

Strength can be measured in a number of ways. One way is RM (repetition maximum) which we will look at on page 103. Measuring a person's grip strength will give some indication, and this can be carried out using a grip strength dynamometer. Power can be measured using the sergeant jump and the standing broad jump.

Safety rules

Safety rules should be written out and recorded in a positive manner. For example, instead of writing 'never train alone', write:

1 Always train with a partner or the instructor present in the training room.

2 Eat at least two hours before training.

3 Change into suitable clothing and footwear.

4 Only train if you feel up to it, especially if you have been dizzy or suffering from flu.

5 Check equipment before using it and report any problems you might find.

6 Warm-up using an aerobic-type activity and stretching all the major muscle groups.

7 Always cool-down after completing the training session, again using an aerobic activity and stretching.

8 Use suitable workloads – not too heavy.

9 Carry out the exercises correctly.

10 Always lift and lower under control.

11 Check out your programme with the instructor or teacher.

Key terms

● muscular endurance
● muscular strength
● overload
● power
● safety

Weight training

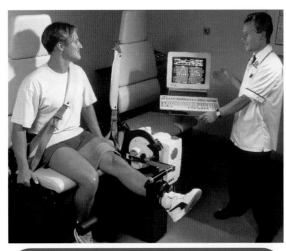

Injury victims may need to use very light weights to regain muscle after their injury. Muscle is lost after injury and this is called muscle *atrophy*. *Hypertrophy* is the opposite, as muscles will get bigger with increased workload

What is it?

Weight training is a form of training that uses progressive resistance, either in the form of actual weight lifted or in terms of the number of times the weight is lifted.

What is it for?

Weight training is used to:

1 increase muscular strength
2 increase muscular endurance
3 increase speed
4 develop muscle bulk or size
5 rehabilitate after illness or injury.

How do I construct a schedule?

A weight training schedule is a programme that sets out in detail what you are intending to achieve and how you intend to achieve it. This will include the use of the training principles, such as FITT (Frequency, Intensity, Time and the Type of work you will carry out in the programme – see page 87).

First decide what you are training for – i.e. the purpose. The answer to this will affect:

1 the number of exercises
2 the exercises for each muscle group
3 the weight used
4 the number of repetitions
5 the number of sets
6 how fast the exercise is done
7 how long the rest is between sets
8 the frequency of training.

Refer back to the principles of training set out on pages 85–9.

1 Number of exercises

If you are using circuit weight training, or the sets method of training, 8–12 exercises taken from the core programme shown on the chart on the right would be suitable. The core programme is a set of exercises that are suitable for general but not specific use. They would suit most people, to start them off on their schedule.

2 Exercises for each muscle group

In the early stages of weight training, it would be most suitable to follow a core programme set by the teacher/instructor.

Body builders need to lift weights many times and use supplements to enhance their muscular development

3 Weight used

About 40% to 50% of your 5 RM. RM means repetition maximum (or rep. max.). 1 RM is the maximum a person can lift once. So 5 RM is the most a person can lift 5 times.

First, estimate what weight you think will be your RM and try to do 5 reps. As soon as you realize it's too heavy or too light stop and re-set the weight. Don't waste energy trying to lift too much, or too many times, or you will not find your *true* 1 or 5 RM.

4 Number of repetitions

In the sets method of training it is usual to make 10 repetitions per set.

5 Number of sets

Normally 3 sets of 10 repetitions are performed, but for the first couple of weeks it is probably best to start with 2 sets of 10 repetitions.

6 How fast the exercise is done

It is more important, when starting out, to be in control of the weights than to work too quickly, but the repetitions should be done in 1.5–2 seconds.

7 How long the rest is between sets

Recovery between sets is normally about 1–2 minutes, if working with a training partner or partners. Taking turns is probably about the same time.

8 Frequency of training

This type of weight training is not so demanding or intensive as pure strength training, so it does not need the same amount of rest between sessions, but with novice performers one day between sessions is advisable.

Task

Use the information on weight training to construct a weight training schedule (PEP) for six weeks.

Key terms

- frequency
- intensity
- muscle bulk
- repetition maximum (rep. max., RM)
- repetitions
- sets
- weight training

No.	Exercise	Muscle group	Weight	Reps	Sets	Rest	Date
1	Bench press						
2	Sit-ups						
3	Bar dips						
4	Lat. pull down						
5	Seated rowing						
6	Hip flexor						
7	Leg curl						
8	Leg extension						
9	Shoulder press						
10	Bicep curl						
11	Cycle ergometer						
12	Chin-ups						

A weight training exercise schedule (PEP) might look something like this, before inserting all the required data

Different ways that muscles contract

There are some points to know before you can start on your weight training PEP. Muscles cannot push! They can only *pull!* This is called a muscle contraction. There are a number of different ways that a muscle can contract and you need to know two of these: **isotonic** and **isometric**.

Isotonic contractions

An isotonic contraction occurs when the muscle both contracts and works over a range of movement.

Example: In the dumb-bell curl, the bicep muscle contracts to bend the arm at the elbow, while the tricep relaxes. To lower the dumb-bell under control, the tricep contracts and the bicep relaxes. When muscles work in this way they are said to be **antagonistic** (see Biceps and triceps, page 125).

The dumb-bell curl

There are many examples of isotonic muscle action in sports and games, perhaps walking or running are the simplest ones. Most training uses isotonic contractions such as the bicep curl shown below left.

Isometric contractions

An isometric contraction is when the muscle contracts but stays in a fixed position, neither shortening nor lengthening.

Example: In the dumb-bell curl (bicep curl), if the movement is stopped when the forearm is at right angles to the upper arm, and then the position is held for several seconds, this is an isometric contraction. The muscle is working (contracting) without movement.

There aren't many examples of isometric contractions used during sporting action but a rugby scrum is one example. A test of isometric strength is sometimes used in the World's Strongest Man competition. This involves tests such as holding a magnum of champagne in each hand and at arm's length for as long as possible.

Strength can be improved using isometric contractions but the strength gains tend to be less and over a smaller range of movement. One example of an isometric exercise would be to press the palms together in front of the chest for several seconds and then relax.

Task 1

Think of two other instances when an isometric muscle contraction takes place in a sporting situation.

Lesson 34: Different ways that muscles contract

Weight machines and free weights

Weight training may be carried out on a machine (e.g. a multi-gym) or using 'free weights' (i.e. barbells and/or dumb-bells). Each has advantages and disadvantages and some of these are set out below.

Weight machines

Advantages

- safe
- convenient
- technologically advanced
- beginners find them easier than free weights.

Disadvantages

- they are expensive!

Task 2

Name a sport and then give an example of a situation in that sport when extra strength would be an advantage. For example, striking the ball in football.

Free weights

Advantages

- used by top athletes (presses, pulls and squats)
- exercises can be performed which you cannot do on machines
- uses explosive strength
- more variety of exercises.

Disadvantages

- requires spotters
- skill involved.

Most elite athletes gain their strength by using free weights as the weight has to be controlled by the athlete, and many more specific exercises can be performed.

However, when training with heavy weights, spotters are needed to assist in case the athlete loses control of the bar.

Key terms

- **isometric**
- **isotonic**

There are advantages and disadvantages to both weight machines and free weights

105

Bones

In order to understand a little more about muscular strength and muscular endurance, it is necessary to learn more about bones, joints and muscles. These form the structure of the body, which is known as the anatomy. We have already learned something about the function of the body, or physiology, when we looked at the circulatory and respiratory systems.

Think of the walls of a house as a framework upon which the rest of the house is formed. Water, gas and electricity supplies are also necessary to make the house function. The bones of the skeleton might seem to be just a framework on which our body is built, but it is much more than that. Some bones are hollow and inside them is the red bone

marrow from which our blood is formed. This produces most of the cells of the blood and is vital to our lives. Diseases of the blood can cause cancer or leukaemia, and we often hear about bone marrow transplants.

Bone growth

All bones are formed from cartilage, except the clavicle and some parts of the cranium (skull). Bones begin to grow before children are born, and as growth takes place the cartilage, which forms their temporary skeleton, is hardened into bone by the addition of calcium and other minerals. Bone growth begins in the centre of each bone. In a long bone this is in the centre of the shaft.

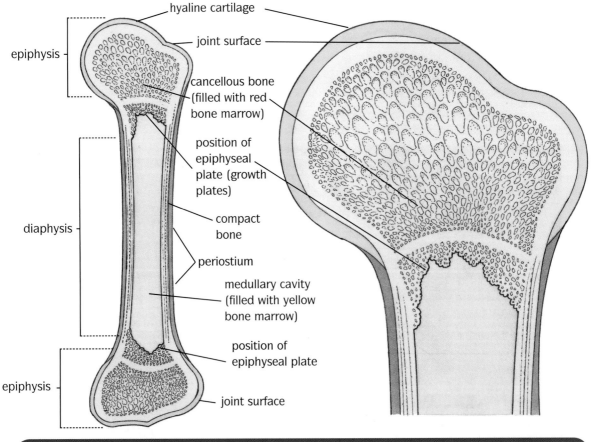

hyaline cartilage

joint surface

epiphysis

cancellous bone (filled with red bone marrow)

position of epiphyseal plate (growth plates)

compact bone

diaphysis

periostium

medullary cavity (filled with yellow bone marrow)

position of epiphyseal plate

epiphysis

joint surface

Long bones act as levers, make both red and white blood cells, store minerals and provide attachment points for muscles.

Growth takes place upwards, downwards and around the central marrow cavity, then secondary growth appears at both ends. Cartilage remains between the areas until bone growth is completed. These areas are known as growth plates. This process of development from cartilage to bone is known as ossification.

Definitions

epiphysis (plural: epiphyses)	the end of a long bone
diaphysis	the shaft of a long bone
cartilage	a dense, elastic, connective tissue which cushions and connects many bones in the skeleton
periosteum	a tough membrane which surrounds the bone
compact bone	a substance beneath the periosteum, forming the shaft of a long bone
cancellous bone	a spongy substance found inside the compact bone
calcium	mineral vital for healthy bones; best sources are milk, cheese and yoghurt – but choose low fat!

Task 1

We only need most minerals in small amounts, but which foodstuffs provide us with those we require?

Bones as a factor affecting performance

Bones form part of our lean body mass. Bone size determines body size and, to a large extent, somatotype (see page 40). When you took your wrist girth size, you determined your frame size. Your bones scores influenced your mesomorph score when taking your somatotype (page 56).

Because bones influence body composition, they also affect participation and performance in physical activity.

Health issues about bones

- Bones of the skeleton are alive.
- A child's skeleton is replaced cell by cell every two years.
- Bones stop growing in length after about age 16–18 but still increase in density.
- After about age 35 bones deteriorate.

Osteoporosis

With age the density and strength of bones is reduced. It has been shown that astronauts lose bone density during long missions in space, in the weightless conditions of zero gravity. This is because we need regular exercise or training of a weight bearing nature to keep our bones dense and strong – walking or climbing stairs, say, as opposed to swimming or other activities in which body weight is supported. While the gradual loss of bone density is a natural process as we get old, in some people far too much bone is lost. Their skeleton becomes weak and fragile and they break bones easily. This condition is called osteoporosis. A good diet and regular exercise can prevent osteoporosis or slow it done if it has begun.

How to look after your bones

- We know we must eat a balanced diet that is also rich in calcium. This helps our bones.
- Weight-bearing exercises are best for our bones. These include: skipping, jumping, running up and down stairs, brisk walking and ball games.
- Avoid smoking and too much alcohol.

Key terms

- anatomy
- calcium
- cartilage
- ossification
- physiology
- structure

Functions of the bones and skeleton

If we look at a skeleton we can see that bones come together and form a variety of joints, which, when they work together, act as levers. This allows us to make a variety of movements called fine movements (such as threading a needle with cotton) and coarse movements (such as throwing a javelin).

Muscles are attached to the bones by **tendons** and these allow us to apply power and movement.

Another function of the skeleton is protection. The cranium protects the brain, and the spine (or vertebral column) protects the spinal chord. The ribs, which form the chest, protect the heart and lungs, and some of the abdominal organs such as the liver, the spleen and, to some extent, the stomach and kidneys. Below the abdomen is the ilium and ischium, behind which are the bladder and the lower intestines, and, in a woman, the reproductive organs.

The skeleton is also a store in which we keep calcium. This gives bones rigidity or hardness.

Classification of bones

In general, bones are classified according to their function.

Protection: flat (or plate) bones

The ribs, scapula, patella, cranium, sternum, clavicle and ilium are flat bones and these tend to be associated with protection.

Protection: irregular bones

The vertebrae are irregular bones that protect.

Levers: long bones

The bones of the limbs are long bones and are associated with levers, this includes phalanges, metatarsals and metacarpals.

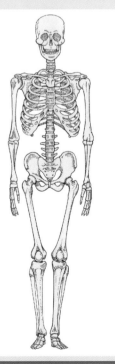

As these pictures show, it is the skeleton which helps give the body its shape, supporting it, keeping it in position and providing a structure for the muscles to be attached to.

Therefore the skeleton's functions are:

- to allow movement and support the body in the upright position
- to protect the vital organs
- the production of blood
- to give the body its shape.

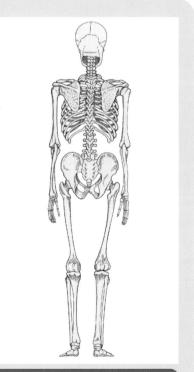

The lower skeleton is for stability, the upper for mobility

Bones in the upper body

The clavicle

The clavicle (or collar bone) is a flat, slightly curved bone, which helps to keep our shoulders back. This bone is vulnerable in sport as a blow to it may cause it to break. This is often easy to diagnose, as the bone will look irregular and there may be a deformity at the shoulder, while the person will hold their lower arm across their waist and will suffer a lot of pain at the site of the injury (see page 138).

The scapula and humerus

The scapula (or shoulder blade) forms a joint with the head of the humerus (the bone between the elbow and the shoulder) which has a globular head. The head fits loosely into a shallow cup on the scapula. It is held in position by **ligaments,** which join the bones together. Just below the head is the neck, which is often where the humerus is fractured. This can be diagnosed in a similar way to a break of the clavicle. The humerus and the ulna, make up the elbow joint.

The radius and ulna

It may sometimes be difficult to remember which is which, but the **U**lna is the one that is **U**nderneath. The radius and the ulna both have a slightly pointed end to them, but the one in the radius extends just a little further. If the radius is fractured these positions are reversed and this is known as a Colle's fracture. This injury is sometimes caused by landing badly on the wrist or putting out the hands to stop running into a wall. This is one good reason for not using the hands when turning quickly against the gymnasium walls during relay races and sprints.

The wrist and hand

The wrist bones are called carpals (short bones). You can remember this by: 'Carpals and Cuffs'. The bones in the hand are called metacarpals and in the fingers, phalanges. All of these are classified as long bones. There are three phalanges in each finger and two in each thumb.

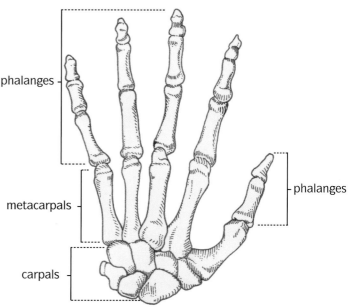

The bones of the hand (viewed from the back of the left hand)

Task 3

a Write down a numbered list of the functions of the skeleton. Use at least one sentence for each.

b Write out two numbered lists, one for functions of flat bones and one for long bones.

c Explain the functions of flat bones and long bones.

Key terms

- **carpals, metacarpals and phalanges**
- **clavicle**
- **flat (or plate) bones**
- **humerus**
- **ilium and ischium**
- **irregular bones**
- **ligaments**
- **long bones**
- **radius and ulna**
- **scapula**

Bones in the lower body

The pelvis

The ileum (or hip bone) and the pubis, together with the sacrum and the coccyx, form the pelvis. The sacrum and the coccyx are part of the vertebral column (see page 112.)

The femur

The femur is often known as the thigh-bone and it is the largest bone in the body. It is similar to the humerus in the arm in that it has a globular head, which fits neatly into a cup-shaped cavity in the hip-bone.

The meeting point of the hip-bone and the head of the femur is the hip joint. Again, like the humerus, below the head of the femur is the neck, which often becomes brittle with age and in old people it is often fractured. At the end of the femur there are two condyles (or rounded ends) which join the condyles of the tibia to form the knee joint. The patella (or kneecap) glides on the condyles of the femur.

When you measured the width across your humerus and across your femur in order to assess your bone size for your somatype (pages 56–7), the width across the condyles was what you were actually measuring.

An artificial hip joint

The joint between the femur and the hip is a ball and socket joint (see page 115). These sometimes become worn through overwork, age or wear through certain sports activities, and they have to be replaced. This is known as a hip replacement. The ball at the top of the femur is sawn off and replaced with an artificial one. This is now a very successful operation.

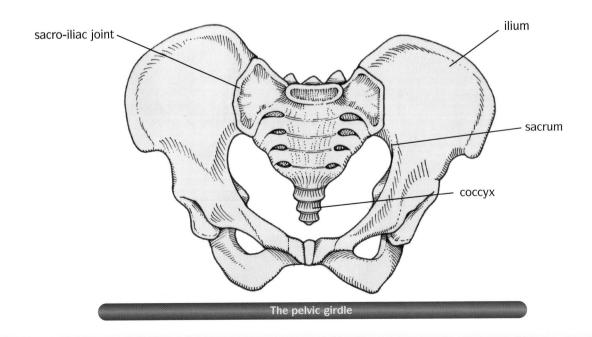

The pelvic girdle

sacro-iliac joint

ilium

sacrum

coccyx

The tibia and fibula

Below the knee are two bones which together are called the lower leg. The bigger of the two is called the tibia. We often call this the shin-bone and in some contact sports we use shin guards or shin pads to protect it.

The fibula is a slimmer bone and is on the outside of the leg. The weight of the body is taken on the tibia, which together with the femur forms the knee joint.

> ## Task 1
>
> **a** Name the three long bones in the leg.
> **b** What are bones of this type required to do?

The tarsals, metatarsals and phalanges

The bones of the ankle are called the tarsals (short bones) and can be remembered as 'Tarsals and Toes'. So we can now distinguish between the bones that form the wrist and those that form the ankle:

Carpals and Cuffs   =   wrist
Tarsals and Toes   =   ankle

After the tarsals are the metatarsals along the length of the foot and the bones of the toes are the phalanges, as of course are the fingers. Remember that these are long bones.

> ## Task 2
>
> List two short bones and state where to find each of them.

Key terms

- coccyx
- femur
- fibula
- ilium
- metatarsals
- phalanges
- sacrum
- short bones
- tarsals
- tibia

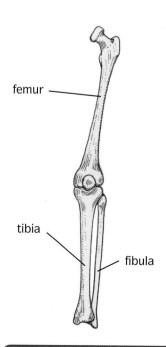

The bones of the legs

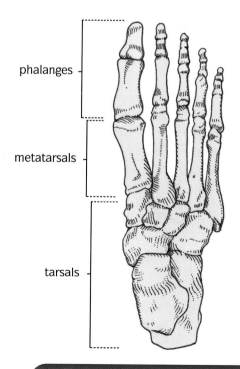

The bones of the feet (viewed from above the right foot)

The vertebral column

The vertebral column is very versatile. It has strength and is flexible but when we want to we can make it rigid. We can use it as a lever and it also protects the spinal chord.

The ribs

We have twelve ribs and it is their job to protect the organs of the chest and the upper abdomen. They are attached to the vertebral column at the back and to the sternum (or breastbone) in front. The last two are free and are called floating ribs. There are small muscles between the ribs called the intercostal muscles, which raise the ribs to expand the chest to enable us to breathe (see pages 72–3).

The vertebrae

The vertebral column consists of 33 bones, or vertebrae, which are divided into five groups. Starting from the top there are:

- *seven in the cervical region* which form the neck, and allow a variety of movement
- *twelve in the thoracic region* (the chest or thorax). Ten of these vertebrae raise a pair of ribs when we breathe
- *five in the lumbar region* (the lower back). The discs in this region are relatively large and this allows us more mobility
- *five in the sacrum* which in adulthood are fused together and work with the hip-bones making it part of the pelvic girdle
- *four in the coccyx* (which used to form our tail).

All the vertebrae fit neatly together to protect the spinal chord. Between each vertebrae is an intervertebral disc. These make up almost a third of the total length of the spine.

The discs are very delicate and if put out of action by slipping out of place or tearing, the patient is said to have 'slipped a disc', a very painful condition.

The vertebrae are classified as irregular bones. Other irregular bones can be found in the face.

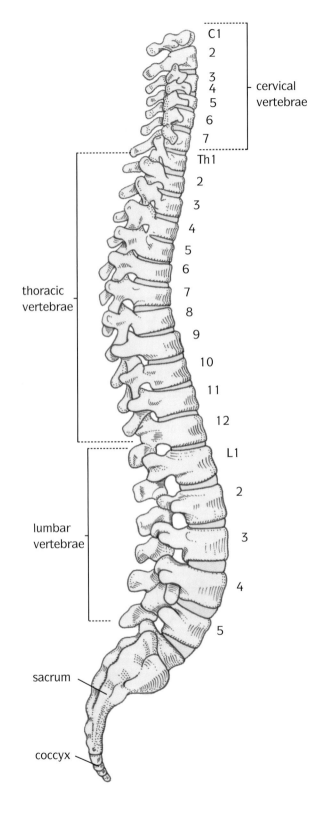

The vertebral column showing the regions of the spine

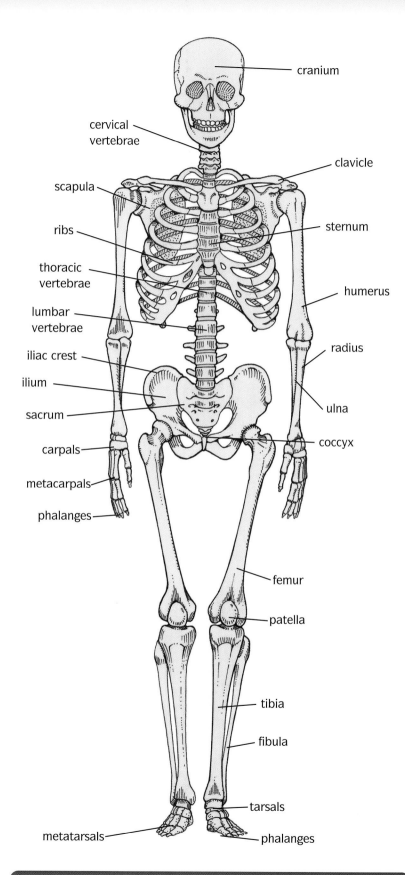

cranium

cervical
vertebrae

clavicle

scapula

sternum

ribs

thoracic
vertebrae

humerus

lumbar
vertebrae

radius

iliac crest

ilium

sacrum

ulna

coccyx

carpals

metacarpals

phalanges

femur

patella

tibia

fibula

tarsals

metatarsals

phalanges

The main bones in the human body

Task

Draw up a table for the different types of bones using these headings: long bone; short bone; flat bone; irregular bone. Using the bones labelled on the diagram on this page add each bone to the table under the correct heading.

Key terms

- **cervical vertebrae**
- **coccyx**
- **irregular bones**
- **lumbar vertebrae**
- **sacrum**
- **sternum**
- **thoracic vertebrae**
- **thorax**
- **vertebral column**

Joints of the body

joint	a place where two or more bones meet

If our bodies were not jointed we would be very awkward and ungainly, and our activities would be extremely restricted. Our backs are flexible because the vertebral column is made up of a number of small bones. If our upper limbs were not jointed we could not feed as we do. If our lower limbs were not jointed we would not be able to stand, as our body is on too small a base to remain stable. Even so, a slight wind could topple us over if our muscles were not constantly moving and adjusting our **balance** by means of our joints.

Jointed bones and flexible fingers have enabled us to attain things no other animal is capable of doing. As an example, monkeys cannot oppose (i.e. press together) their thumb to their other fingers to form the pincer movement that is one of the main reasons for our dominance.

This mobility is created by the special type of joint between the first metacarpal bone and the one next to it.

The joints in the upper limbs are for mobility and the joints in the lower limbs are for stability.

Synovial joints

In order to prevent pain through the friction that might be caused by the bones rubbing together, the ends of the bones in a synovial joint are covered with a layer of thick cartilage, known as hyaline cartilage. The cartilage is made up of a group of cells that are surrounded by fluid. The cartilage is elastic and this enables it to cushion and therefore protect the ends of the bones involved in the joint. Surrounding a synovial joint is a tough capsule, which is reinforced by ligaments. Inside the capsule is a synovial membrane which produces synovial fluid to lubricate the joint.

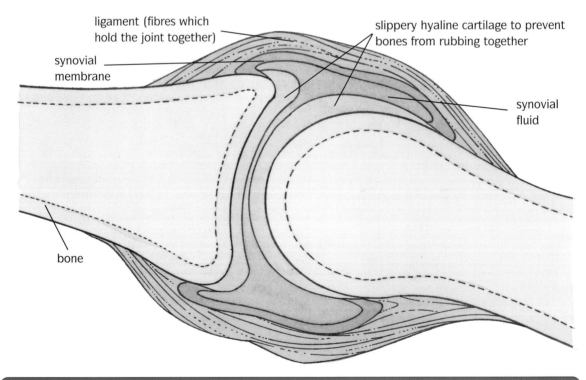

ligament (fibres which hold the joint together)

slippery hyaline cartilage to prevent bones from rubbing together

synovial membrane

synovial fluid

bone

A synovial joint (freely movable)

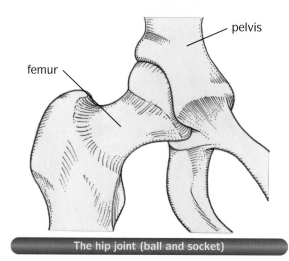

The hip joint (ball and socket)

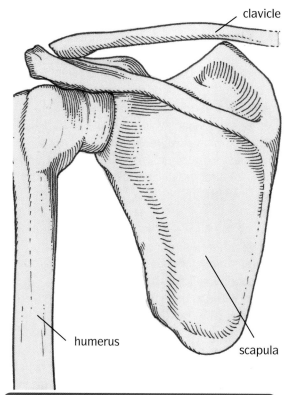

The shoulder joint (ball and socket)

The hip and shoulder joints

Both of these joints are called ball and socket joints because the head of the long bone, either the humerus in the arm or the femur in the leg, is shaped like a ball, and this fits into a socket in the shape of a cup. The hip and shoulder joints are very similar in make-up, as the bones are covered with cartilage and reinforced with ligaments, but the shoulder joint has more freedom than the hip and is capable of more variety and a bigger range of movement.

Movement at joints

All joints have movement but the ability and freedom of movement varies from joint to joint. In GCSE PE we are concerned with **flexion, extension, adduction, abduction** and **rotation.** In the shoulder joint, all of these movements can be performed quite easily as the head of the humerus can be rotated either forwards (such as when bowling a cricket ball) or backwards (such as when swimming back crawl).

These movements can be performed by the hip joint, but to a much lesser extent – consider the example of bowling a cricket ball! The shoulder can also be extended, as when a swimmer swings the arm backwards from the shoulder joint in preparation for a racing dive, and flexed when they bring it forward as they dive into the water.

Task 1

a Consider the shoulder joint and give a further example from a sport of your choice for each type of movement possible: flexion; extension; adduction; abduction; rotation.

b Now repeat task **a** for the hip joint.

Key terms

- **abduction**
- **adduction**
- **extension**
- **flexibility, mobility, stability**
- **flexion**
- **hyaline cartilage**
- **rotation**
- **synovial fluid**
- **synovial joint**

The knee joint

This is the largest and most complex joint, in which the tibia is hinged on the femur so that the leg can be bent (flexion) or straightened (extension). Squats or the seated leg press might be a good example of this, though perhaps the sergeant jump is the best; but the most common is when a footballer bends the lower leg at the knee preparing to kick the ball (flexion) and straightens it when striking the ball (extension).

Flexing the knee joint is like the swing of a pendulum and requires a minimum of effort at the joint, which prevents it from wearing out too soon. This joint can also be slightly rotated. The knee joint is an articulation of the condyles (the rounded ends) of the femur and the tibia, and it should be remembered that the fibula plays no part in it. As well as a hinge joint, it is a synovial joint – there is no socket, only two smooth shallow surfaces that are in contact. Two short but very strong ligaments about the thickness of the little finger prevent the bones from sliding apart.

These ligaments are called the cruciate ligaments and they tie the bones together very efficiently by crossing inside the joint. These are the ligaments often injured by footballers in hard tackles. It is often a very severe injury and can in some cases end a player's career. Paul Gasgcoine suffered this injury when playing for Tottenham Hotspur.

Inside the joint there are semi-lunar cartilages on the condyles of the tibia and they are there for lubrication rather than stability. We often hear of a sportsperson having 'cartilage trouble', which happens when the cartilage is torn, often following a sudden twist of the knee. There is a greater strain put on the knee than on any other joint in the body, and it is not uncommon for a sportsperson to play until their knees can no longer hold out! Because of the strain on the knee it produces more synovial fluid than the other synovial joints.

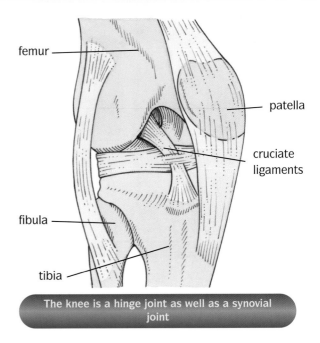

The knee is a hinge joint as well as a synovial joint

Elbow joint

The elbow is a hinge joint between the humerus and ulna, and it also has a pivot joint between the ulna and radius which allows us to rotate the elbow. The hinge joint enables us to bend the arm (flexion) or straighten it (extension), as when doing curls. The most common example of flexion and extension of the elbow joint occurs when we bend our arm to put food into our mouth. The muscles that flex the joint are on the front (biceps) and the muscles that extend it are on the back of the arm (triceps).

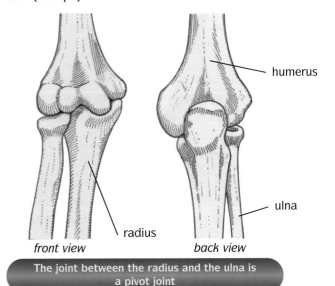

front view　　　　*back view*

The joint between the radius and the ulna is a pivot joint

The wrist joint

The wrist joint is another complex joint and more than just a hinge joint. Not only can we bend it (flexion) and straighten it (extension) but we can turn the hand inwards (adduction) and outwards (abduction). This allows for very complex movements, such as when the cricket bowler bowls spin.

Joints of the fingers

The fingers can be made into a fist (flexion), e.g. gripping a tennis ball, or straightened (extension) e.g. releasing the ball when bowling underarm in rounders. We can open the fingers (abduction) and close them (adduction).

Spin bowling requires a complex movement of the wrist joint

The ankle joint

Yet another hinge joint, this enables us to bend the foot up (flexion), e.g. leading leg when hurdling, and to point the toes down (extension), e.g. pointing the toes while bouncing in the air when trampolining. These movements are also known as dorsiflexion, bending the toes towards the tibia, and plantaflexion, when bending the toes away from the tibia. When we turn the foot inwards (inversion) or outwards (eversion), it is as a result of a gliding movement between the tarsal bones.

Task 2

Draw up a table with two columns. In one column list these five joints. In the other indicate the movement possibilities of each one.

Key terms

- eversion
- gliding
- hinge joint
- inversion
- semi-lunar cartilage
- synovial joint

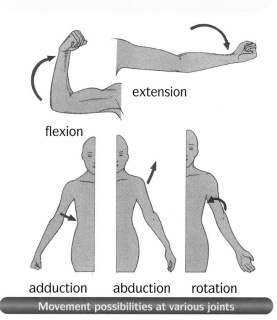

extension

flexion

adduction   abduction   rotation

Movement possibilities at various joints

117

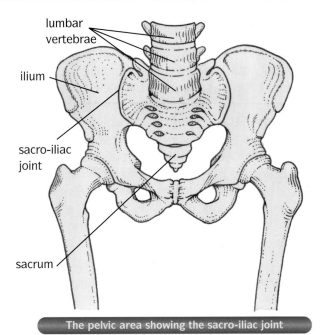

lumbar vertebrae

ilium

sacro-iliac joint

sacrum

The pelvic area showing the sacro-iliac joint

The sacro-iliac joint

The sacro-iliac joint is another example of a synovial joint, but this time it is one with very little movement. It does allow us slight rotation of the sacrum between the hip-bones, and this acts on the same principle as the hinge joint. It helps to take the strain for the spinal chord (much the same as the discs that are between the vertebrae in your vertebral column) when doing jumping movements, such as landing when jumping from a box.

Cartilaginous joints

Cartilaginous joints are found where bones are joined with cartilage between. This type of joint is found in the spine. Whereas synovial joints have a joint capsule and synovial membrane, cartilaginous joints do not. We have quite free movement in the neck region where the first cervical vertebrae, called the atlas (because it takes the weight of the cranium), and the second vertebrae, called the axis (because it allows the atlas to swivel on it), form a pivot joint which allows us to rotate our neck. Lower down in the vertebral column our movement is more restricted, but we can bend (flexion), straighten (extension) and rotate the spine.

Joints and movement

So some joints have lots of movement (the shoulder, hip and thumb are good examples) and some have less and more restricted movement (as we have just seen the vertebral column is an example of this). But to bend, turn or twist your body you need a joint to act.

In any joint that has movement, ligaments, muscles and tendons hold the joint together. At the end of the bones there is cartilage to prevent injury, rubbing and pain, and the joint is surrounded with a joint capsule full of a special liquid called synovial fluid, as you might find oil in a mechanical joint. This fluid prevents friction as the joint works. We move our joints continually, even when we are asleep, but unless we injure them we are often not aware of them.

Joints are very important in sport. Over-stretching can injure them but flexibility exercises allow them to have a greater range of movement. Although it is generally accepted that arthritis is hereditary, some sources also suggest that joint injuries that are not allowed to heal properly can also contribute to this condition.

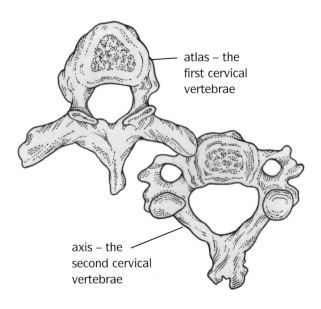

atlas – the first cervical vertebrae

axis – the second cervical vertebrae

The topmost vertebrae in the spinal column, the atlas and axis

These drills involve adduction and abduction

In football, the throw-in can involve extension and rotation

Bowling underarm involves extension and flexion

Task 3

a   Working with a partner, take it in turns to demonstrate a simple movement and ask your partner to explain the movement. For example, bending the arm demonstrates flexion at a hinge joint.

b   Working with a partner, take it in turns to name a type of joint, and ask them to demonstrate all the types of movement possibilities at that joint. For example, hinge joint elbow = flexion, extension, slight rotation.

c   Working with a partner, mime some sporting activities, e.g. cricket bowling. Work out together what joints are involved and the types of movement taking place. For example, shoulder (ball and socket) = rotation.

Key terms

● cartilaginous joints
● friction
● joint capsule
● ligaments
● muscles
● sacro-iliac joint
● synovial fluid
● tendons

Muscles and fat

In order to find your somatotype it was necessary to measure your body fat at certain points on your body (see page 55). Skinfold measurements were taken on the right side of your body at three different points, or sites. Beneath this layer of fat is a sheet of tough fibrous tissue, which is very strong. This forms a cover for all the muscles and increases their power.

Beneath the surface of the skin is one place where we store our fat, as we noted earlier when studying somatotyping, and we took measurements in order to compare the amount of fat stored at different sites in the body. We noted that it varied from place to place and from individual to individual and from male to female. We need this fat as it is very effective in storing heat, which is why thin people feel the cold much more than fat people.

Body mass index (BMI)

A very useful way to measure your body fatness is by using the **body mass index (BMI)**.

The BMI is calculated by taking your weight in kilograms and then dividing it by your height in metres squared. The result can then be checked against this table.

Healthy	20–25
Overweight	25–30
Obese	over 30

For example:

weight		60 kg
height		1 m 65 cm
height squared		2.72
60 / 2.72	=	22
22	=	healthy!

Task 1

Take your height and weight from your record sheet (or retake them) and work out your body mass index.

Lean body mass

All our body parts add up to make the overall weight of our body. Our weight without fat is known as our **lean body mass**. This includes our muscles, bones and organs. Therefore, if we find our total body fat content and subtract this from our total body weight, we are left with the weight of our lean body mass.

Task 2

In task **a** on page 40, you measured an estimate of your 'desirable' body weight using your wrist girth measurement to determine your frame size and then reading a score from a table.

Check back on your result. Were you within the range, over or under your desirable bodyweight? How does this compare with your BMI result? For example, were you within the desirable weight range and between 20 and 25 on the BMI scale?

Activity is an important part of maintaining a healthy weight

Three types of muscle tissue

The muscles of the body each fall into one of three groups and this classification is very important.

1 Voluntary or skeletal muscles

These muscles are made up of cylindrical fibres and are under the control of our will (so they are voluntary). All these muscles are attached to the skeleton (skeletal). These muscles make up about 40% of the weight of a man, but less for a woman because women have a higher ratio of fat. Muscles are made up of protein, and when we eat fish or meat, which is protein, we are actually eating the muscle of the animal.

The skeletal muscles are usually long and thin and because they cannot push they are usually paired up. One muscle bends the joint (flexion) and the other straightens it (extension). In order to get full movement while one muscle contracts the other must relax (**isotonic contraction**). If both contract then no movement takes place (**isometric contraction**). These pairs of muscles are called antagonists.

2 Involuntary muscles

These muscles, as the name suggests, are not under our control. They can be found in the organs of the body, such as the digestive, circulatory and urinary systems, and they contract and relax automatically.

They are controlled by the involuntary nervous system. The muscles are made of spindle-shaped fibres.

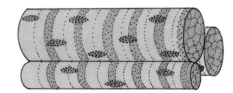

voluntary muscle tissue (striated muscle)

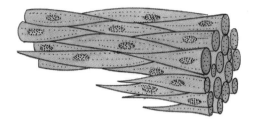

involuntary muscle tissue (smooth muscle)

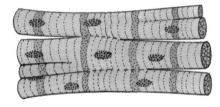

cardiac muscle tissue

The three types of muscle tissue

3 Cardiac muscle

Cardiac muscle is found in the wall of the heart. We cannot control when it contracts and relaxes, so the cardiac muscle is also involuntary. This type of muscle is made up of interlaced fibres, which help the nervous impulses, sent and controlled by a centre in the brain, to regulate our pulse rate and the force of our heartbeat. The main factor concerning the cardiac muscle is that as long as it has a good blood supply, it never tires.

Key terms

- **body mass index (BMI)**
- **cardiac**
- **involuntary**
- **lean body mass**
- **skinfolds**
- **somatotype**
- **voluntary**

Task 3

Write down the name of one place in the body where the muscles may be beyond our control (involuntary), and one place where they are under our control (voluntary).

Muscle fibres

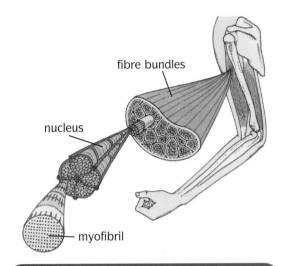

fibre bundles

nucleus

myofibril

Muscle fibres are made up of tiny threadlike myofibrils

Muscles are made up of many muscle cells or muscle fibres, each of which contain many myofibrils. The muscle fibres can be slow twitch or fast twitch. We all have both types in our muscles in different quantities, and what we have appears to be handed down from our parents in our genes.

Slow twitch fibres are deep red in colour and they have a good oxygen supply which we know is necessary to supply energy to the working muscle. These muscles contract slowly but they can work for long periods under great stress.

Fast twitch fibres are white and work much more quickly, but they also tire more quickly. It is easy to remember that endurance athletes tend to have more slow twitch fibres, while speed athletes, especially sprinters, tend to have more fast twitch fibres.

Task 4

Think about the types of exercise studied earlier: aerobic and anaerobic (page 82–4). Which of these two words would you associate with fast twitch fibres and which would you associate with slow twitch fibres? Give reasons for your answer.

Sprinters have fast twitch fibres

Marathon runners have slow twitch fibres

Understanding muscles

Here are some points to remember which will help you understand muscles.

One of the features of the skeleton is that it provides an attachment for muscles, and a feature of muscle fibres is that they can contract, or pull against the skeleton in order to move. What they cannot do is push!

Most muscles are long and thin, but when they contract they get shorter and thicker, e.g. the bicep.

We have seen that muscles are attached to bones by **tendons**. Because muscles cannot push to make joints work they are arranged in antagonistic pairs. These are the muscles which we stretch when we work on mobility/flexibility training.

Although muscles are attached at both ends, one end is called the origin and is fixed to something rigid. The other end, called the insertion, is fixed to the bone that moves.

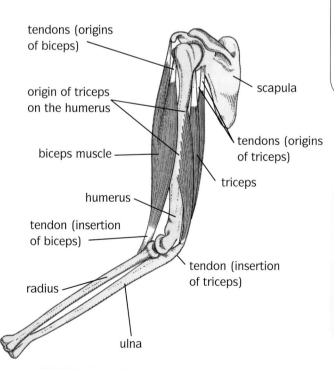

tendons (origins of biceps)

origin of triceps on the humerus

biceps muscle

humerus

tendon (insertion of biceps)

radius

ulna

scapula

tendons (origins of triceps)

triceps

tendon (insertion of triceps)

The origins and insertions of the biceps and triceps

Muscle tone

Muscle cells are never all resting at the same time. Some are always ready for action, day and night. This action or activity is called **muscle tone**. This action of the muscles helps them to become trained and firm while they can also feel elastic because the fibres are always in tension. It takes a lot of our energy to maintain muscle tone and therefore this muscular activity is said to be metabolically expensive.

Metabolic rate is the speed at which we use up our energy. The voluntary muscles, which use a lot of energy, would use up even more if they were not attached by tendons which are not made of muscle fibre and so do not burn energy. The closest that muscles come to complete rest is when we are asleep, which is why sleep is so important when people are ill, when young children grow and when muscle is being built.

Task 5

Work with a partner. One of you should choose the elbow joint and the other the knee joint. Each try to work out where the muscle that bends the joint is found and where the muscle that straightens it is.

Key terms

- **antagonists**
- **contract**
- **fast twitch**
- **insertion**
- **muscle tone**
- **origin**
- **slow twitch**
- **tendons**

Muscles of the upper body and upper limbs

Trapezius

The trapezius holds back the shoulders so that if a person has drooping shoulders it indicates a weak trapezius and poor muscle tone. It is attached to the head and neck at the top and to the shoulder below. The function of the trapezius is to lift or elevate the shoulder and to brace it back and rotate the scapula. It can be developed by performing upright rowing and shoulder shrugs in a weight training programme.

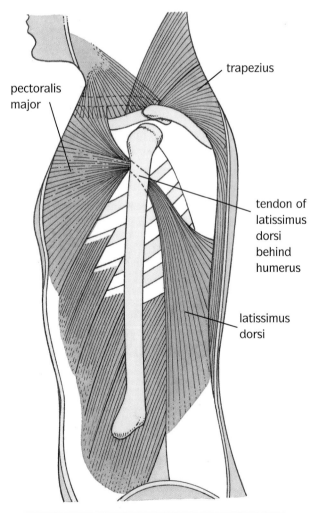

pectoralis major

trapezius

tendon of latissimus dorsi behind humerus

latissimus dorsi

Muscles of the upper body

Latissimus dorsi

Thc latissimus dorsi is a broad sheet of muscle which extends from the lumbar region of the vertebral column to the humerus. It is a big powerful muscle which adducts (adduction) the arms, and rotates (rotation) to draw them back and inwards towards the body. It can be developed by performing lat (lattissimus) pull-downs on a weight machine.

Pectoralis major

The pectoralis major covers the chest. It is another powerful muscle which works to adduct (adduction) the arm and draws the arm forwards to rotate (rotation) it inwards. This is an important muscle in swimming front crawl. A good exercise to improve its strength is the bench press.

Deltoid

The deltoid is the muscle that gives the rounded shape to the shoulder. It is another powerful muscle which abducts (abduction) the arm (moving it away from the body).

This is the muscle mainly responsible for lifting the arm above the head. When the shoulder is dislocated or the humerus is fractured the deltoid is flattened and the shoulder loses its roundness. This is a feature to look for when diagnosing these injuries. Bent-over rowing and bench presses improve its strength.

Abdominals

The abdominals are the muscles that hold your stomach in! But strengthening them will not remove any fat you may have there, although they will act as a support to the abdomen and

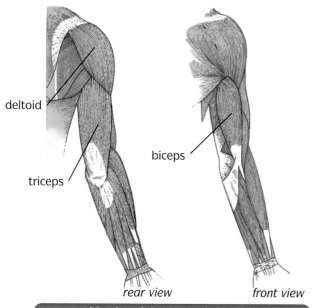

deltoid

biceps

triceps

rear view   *front view*

Muscles of the arm and shoulder

We noted earlier that when muscles contract they can only pull, they cannot push, so in order to work a joint, one muscle works (contracts) while the other relaxes (antagonistic muscles). At the elbow, in order to flex the arm, the biceps contract while the triceps relax. In this movement the biceps act as the flexors, or agonists, and the triceps act as the extensors. When we straighten (extension) the arm, it is the triceps which contract while the biceps relax. The biceps and triceps are involved with throwing actions, such as throwing the javelin.

In order to strengthen the biceps, there are many exercises that can be used, but the most popular are either barbell or dumb-bell curls (see page 104) or preacher curls. To strengthen the triceps use triceps stretches (extension). Good tests for these muscles are chin-ups and parallel bar dips or press-ups.

make you look tighter. The abdominals allow you to flex (flexion) or bend and rotate your trunk and bend to the side.

These muscles can be strengthened using sit-ups, but these can be dangerous if not performed correctly.

It has now been shown that it is not necessary to go through the full range of movement required for sit-ups in order to gain benefit for the abdominal muscles. Crunches give just as good a result to the abdominals and place much less stress on the back.

There are many other exercises that will help to develop the abdominals and most do not require any weights or machines. Poor abdominals can affect **posture** (see page 142).

Biceps and triceps

It will be helpful to describe the biceps and triceps together, because that it just how they work: together.

The bicep is probably the best-known muscle in the body and it is found at the front of the upper arm. The lesser-known triceps are found behind the upper arm.

Task 6

Draw up a table with six columns. In the left-hand column list the names of the muscles on these two pages. Then use the words below as column headings. Add ticks to the columns to show the movements that can be created by each muscle. For example, bicep = flexion.

> Flexion
>
> Extension
>
> Rotation
>
> Adduction
>
> Abduction

Key terms

- **abdominals**
- **biceps and triceps**
- **deltoid**
- **latissimus dorsi**
- **pectoralis major**
- **trapezius**

Muscles of the lower body

The leg muscles are the largest and the strongest muscles in the body and very important in most sports. In sports such as tennis, golf and especially in throwing events in athletics, the initial movement comes from the legs and is finished in the upper body. In fact, the cause of poor performance in these activities is often because of inefficient use of the powerful muscles in the lower body.

Gluteus maximus

The gluteus maximus is another muscle that if poorly developed could cause poor posture. The gluteal muscles form the buttocks and should be referred to in this course by their full name, as above, not 'glutes', as is sometimes used.

As the name implies, the largest of the gluteal muscles is the gluteus maximus. It lies just beneath the skin and is attached to the femur. Its function is to pull the leg backwards (extension). There are many weight-training exercises that will help to develop this muscle, including many of the most popular ones, such as squats, leg presses and lunges.

Quadriceps

The quadriceps are found on the front of the upper leg and, as the name 'quad' implies, there are four of them.

When the doctor tests for reactions at the knee joint it is the patella tendon, which joins the quadriceps to the patella, that he taps. The quadriceps extend (extension), straightening the leg at the knee joint. The most common sporting use it has is kicking a ball, which is why they are sometimes referred to as the kicking muscles. There are numerous exercises suitable to strengthen them, including squats, seated leg presses, leg extensions and lunges.

Hamstrings

The hamstrings are found on the back of the leg and stretch from the bottom part of the pelvis to the tibia. They flex (flexion) to bend the knee, and their tendons can be felt behind the knee because they are so close to the surface. They are of great importance in running. It is vital to warm up the hamstrings properly before sprinting, as this activity can often injure them. Because of their importance in sprinting they are sometimes referred to as the sprinter's muscle. Leg curls are a popular exercise to increase their strength, but they are not as strong as the quadriceps so a lighter weight will be used than when using the leg extension.

Gastrocnemius and soleus

The gastrocnemius and soleus are the muscles that form most of the muscle commonly called the calf muscle. The gastrocnemius starts at the back of the femur and the soleus starts from the back of the tibia and fibula and then they come together to form a tendon which can be seen at the back of the ankle. This is known as the Achilles' tendon. The function of these muscles is to plantar flex (point the toes away from) the foot. They give us that slight spring in our walk. They take a lot of punishment in long distance aerobic work, such as a marathon.

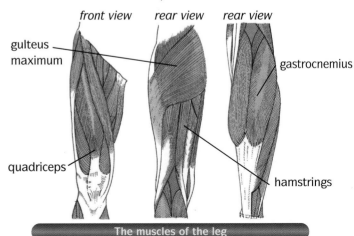

front view   rear view   rear view

gulteus maximum

quadriceps

gastrocnemius

hamstrings

The muscles of the leg

Tendons, ligaments and cartilage

Each of these has an important role to play regarding muscles and joints.

As we have seen, the skeleton provides an attachment for muscles. Muscles are actually attached to bones by **tendons.** When muscles shorten or contract they pull on the bone.

Muscles are never completely relaxed, but are always in a state of slight contraction. This helps us to maintain good posture and supports the body so that we do not fall over. Muscle tone can be improved with exercise, and this also helps to improve posture and provides better support for our internal organs.

Bones are joined to other bones by ligaments, which are elastic and help to support the joint, but the tendons, which join muscle to bone, are less elastic. The ends of bones that form a joint are covered with smooth, slightly flexible material called cartilage. The surface of the cartilage is smooth, to reduce friction between the bones.

Tendons and ligaments can be damaged by the stress put upon them during sporting or training situations. The cruciate ligaments in the knee and the achilles tendon at the back of the ankle are two typical examples of this. The cruciate ligaments are often injured in football tackles while the achilles tendon can be injured in events such as the triple jump. It helps to build up the muscles around the damaged joints when rehabilitating after injury. These types of injury can last for a long time, with long term affects on performance.

Strength

Strength exercises may take various forms, from simple press-ups and sit-ups, to the use of free weights and multi-gyms of various kinds. Whatever method is used, if the exercise increases the muscle girth or size, then the muscle will increase in strength. When muscle increases in girth or size it is known as muscle

Throwing a javelin well depends on a number of factors, not just strength

hypertrophy. However, in strength events such as the javelin, other factors have to be taken into account, such as skill and length of levers.

There are a number of changes that weight training can bring about. Increased muscle mass will produce a firmer-looking body with stronger muscles. Often when people are ill they may lose muscle mass and this is known as muscle **atrophy.** This is another good reason for people to follow a well planned weight training programme.

Weight training can also increase the strength of your tendons, ligaments and bone, and this will lower the risk of injury in these areas.

Task 1

a What is the term used to describe muscle wastage? And what is the term used to describe muscle increase?

b Give two examples of the effects that weight training can have on the muscles.

Key terms

- **gastrocnemius**
- **gluteus maximus**
- **hamstrings**
- **injury**
- **muscle tone**
- **posture**
- **strength**

Muscles, strength and endurance

Muscles can be developed to improve their ability to exert force over one dynamic movement, e.g. by making one lift of a maximum weight or load (muscular strength), or they may be developed to exert force using lighter loads but over a number of repetitions (muscular endurance). In this case the endurance factor would only involve one set of muscles, e.g. the abdominal muscles when doing crunches or sit-ups.

The programme you choose to follow will depend on personal circumstances, e.g. your age, event, sporting activity and probably the time you have available to train. However, it is important to know which muscle groups you are going to work on and therefore which exercises you need to use. On the multi-gym you might use the exercises in the table as a core programme which would give all-round development, but this combination of exercises is not designed for any one particular activity – in other words we are not utilizing the principle of specificity.

Task 2

Copy and complete the table below. Use the diagram opposite to help you find all the muscles and then describe in your own words exactly where to find them. For example: quadriceps – found in the front of the leg above the knee.

Key terms

- core programme
- muscular endurance
- muscular strength
- repetitions
- specificity

No.	Muscle group	Position in body
1	Pectorals	
2	Abdominals	
3	Triceps	
4	Latissimus dorsi	
5	Gastrocnemius	
6	Trapezius	
7	Hamstrings	
8	Quadriceps	
9	Deltoid	
10	Biceps	
11	Cardiac	

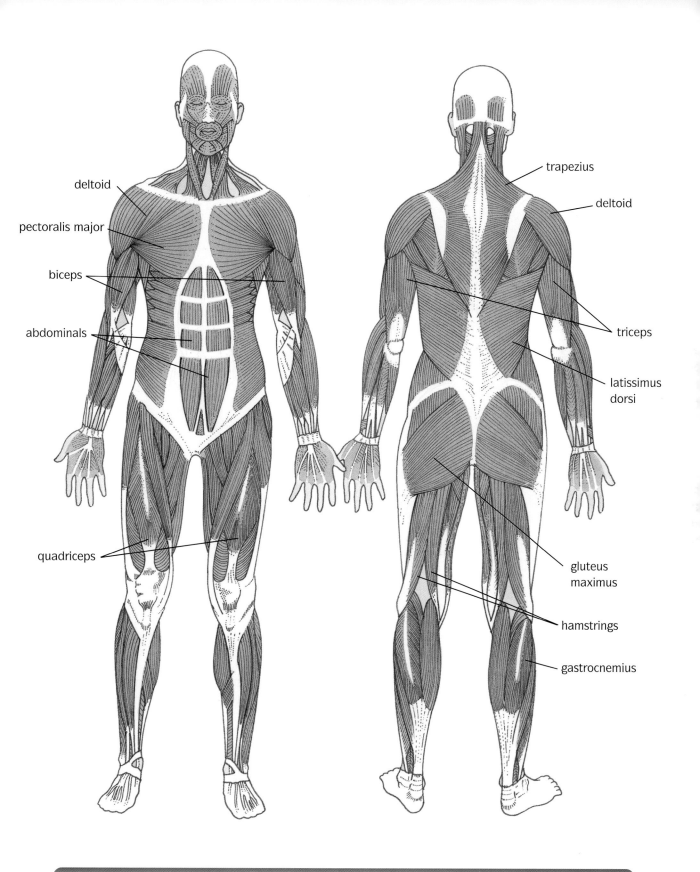

deltoid

pectoralis major

biceps

abdominals

quadriceps

trapezius

deltoid

triceps

latissimus dorsi

gluteus maximus

hamstrings

gastrocnemius

The major muscles in the human body

Flexibility and mobility

Definitions

Flexibiliy	Charles Corbin defines this as: 'The range of motion available in a joint. It is affected by muscle length, joint structure and other factors. A fit person can move the body joints through a full range of motion in work and in play.'

When boys reach puberty, the male sex hormone begins to act on the muscles and they increase in strength. Any malfunction in this process, chronic malnutrition or serious illness can delay this change.

Task 1

Perform some gentle hamstring stretches and then either use a sit-and-reach box, if one is available, or sit on the floor and put the soles of your feet against a gymnastics bench turned so that the top is facing you. Now gently reach forward and measure in centimetres how close you can reach to your toes or how far you can get past them. Reaching your toes is very good. This will measure how flexible you are in your hamstring muscle.

Muscle elasticity

The elasticity in a muscle can be compared with an elastic band which may be stretched by a force but will return to its normal length when the force is withdrawn. The same applies to muscle in tension when we stretch.

Muscles are stretched with exercise and people in certain activities, such as ballet, gymnastics and athletics, perform a lot of flexibility exercises in training in order to increase the range of movement in their joints.

When we perform the stretches as well as increasing the range, we also decrease our susceptibility to muscle injuries.

There are three methods of performing these stretches, which are explained on pages 90–1.

1 Static (active and passive) stretches
2 Ballistic stretches
3 Proprioceptive neuromuscular facilitation (PNF).

Task 2

After a suitable warm-up, work with a partner and try the following assisted (PNF) stretches in order to help you to understand the differences between types of stretches.

Use the hamstring stretch, as in sit and reach.

a Slowly reach towards your toes and hold your furthermost reach for 10 seconds. Record this score on the sit and reach.

b Sit in the same position as before, but this time instead of reaching forward, get your partner to put their hands on your shoulders and push you forwards while you push backwards against them. Hold for 10 seconds.

c Now repeat your proper sit and reach test but get your partner, once again with their hands on your shoulders, to slowly and gently assist you by pushing you into the sit and reach. Hold for 10 seconds. Relax.

d Check your two sit and reach scores, one unassisted and one assisted after the stretch back against your partner's resistance.

Do not force your partner when stretching as this could cause an injury.

Change over and assist your partner in the test.

Cramp

We know that sugar provides the energy needed to make our muscles contract, and when this happens heat is produced – as also happens with a car engine. In our muscles this process produces carbon dioxide, lactic acid and water. When these waste products build up the muscle cannot work and pain from cramp will begin. Then the muscle will stop working until the waste products are removed. This can be avoided by taking some periods of rest for the lactic acid to be removed. As we get fitter we get more efficient and can avoid the onset of cramp for much longer periods.

We have also seen that the higher the intensity of the exercise the more likely we are to experience cramp. Cramp can be eased by slowly stretching the muscle to reduce the pain. For footballers this cramp is usually in the calf or gastrocnemius muscles, and often occurs near the end of a hard match in heavy conditions – and especially to players who are unfit!

Increasing flexibility

To increase flexibility the main areas to work on are the hamstrings, quadriceps, gastrocnemius, groin, back and shoulders. Use static stretches held for 30–40 seconds but never to the point of experiencing pain. Perform three sets of each exercise. As these activities can be performed without the use of special equipment or the need for a special area, they are easy to perform and five times each week would not be excessive.

Safety note

Never use the ballistic method of warming-up or for flexibility, as this is dangerous. The static stretch method also gets better results.

It is noticeable that certain activities suit very young performers. The flexibility of young female gymnasts, for example, is a big advantage in this sport

Points to remember

- As we get older we get less flexible.
- Women are usually more flexible than men.
- We warm up because this increases our flexibility and reduces the risk of injury.
- In warm climates and on warm days we have better flexibility.
- Our body composition (another health-related factor) can affect our flexibility
- When we have an injury to a joint this can affect the flexibility at the joint at the time and perhaps for ever, and so we have to work on this in rehabilitation.

Key terms

- **ballistic stretching**
- **cramp**
- **flexibility**
- **proprioceptive neuromuscular facilitation (PNF)**
- **static (passive) stretching**
- **warm-up**

Controversial and contra-indicated exercises

Contra-indicated exercises are those that go against what we know to be good practice, and they are therefore, at the very least, controversial. That is to say doubts have been raised about their safety.

Thirty years ago there were many exercises that were put into training programmes that we now know are controversial and many would agree that they should be classed as contra-indicated. The reason for them to be considered in this way is usually because they fall into one or more of the following three categories.

1 Hyperextension

This describes exercises that hyperextend the joint. An example might be excessive arching of the back, which might be seen in some gymnastics routines.

Another hyperextension exercise that is now frowned on is cervical extension of the neck – stretching the neck backwards as far as it can go.

2 Hyperflexion

This describes exercises that hyperflex the back. Toe touching is an example and it gains a high rating of danger from many exercise specialists.

Task 3

Think of an exercise that might cause hyperextension and another that might cause hyperflexion. Then work out what you think would be a good alternative and explain why.

3 High impact exercises

Exercises such star jumps, or exercises that require you to jump up and down double-footed on the spot, are considered to have a risk factor when training. Shin splints are one injury thought to be caused by this sort of training. Low impact exercises are recommended, and a suitable one might be skipping on alternate legs.

Task 4

Think of another alternative exercise (other than skipping) which might be considered to be low impact as opposed to high impact.

Sit-ups

Sit-ups have been around for a long time and are one of the prime exercises that fit into the contra-indicated/controversial category. It is now generally accepted that sit-ups with straight legs, and/or hands clasped behind the neck are bad exercises. There are a number of alternatives, but they all require bent legs, with hands either on the chest, to the side, placed on the legs or with fingers at the temples or ears.

It should be remembered that the sports scientists have discovered that we do not need to go through the whole range of sit-up movements to get a good abdominal work-out, and now many people substitute crunches as an alternative exercise. These are thought to be just as effective.

Task 5

Work with a partner and, after an appropriate warm-up, take turns to perform each of the recommended sit-ups for 5–10 repetitions.

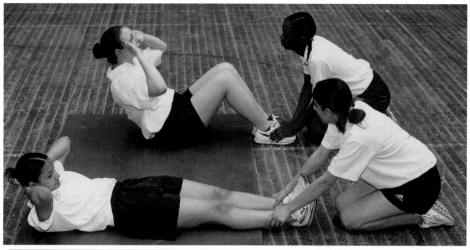

Which one of these sit-up methods is contra-indicated?

Vulnerable areas

Although there are a number of contra-indicated exercises, the ones of main concern are those that involve the neck and the back, and that is why the sit-up is one of them. It also fits the form of a ballistic exercise. We can see from our work on the spinal column and the vertebrae just how vulnerable this area is. Likewise from our study of the knee joint (the most complicated and vulnerable joint in the body), we should now understand why exercises such as star jumps can cause injury to the knee.

Overuse injuries

Injuries from bad exercises are sometimes instant but for many people it is the long-term damage that gradually takes a toll in certain areas. Far too many people who have exercised throughout their lives to keep fit and active as well as to take part and enjoy their sport, end up with a permanent injury, often through no fault of their own.

Many of these injuries are what is known as overuse injuries, brought about by playing too much sport, or being too involved at too young an age. Osgood Schlatter's Disease is a very common condition, particularly in young teenage boys, many of whom have played too much football or other such sport when they were in their early growing years. This condition causes a swelling and tenderness below the patella and often takes a long time to clear, and a lot of sport is missed as a result.

Questions to ask about an exercise

- Does it work the muscle we want it to work?
- Is it intense enough?
- Does it hyperextend?
- Does it hyperflex?
- Is it high impact?
- Does it fit the purpose?

Task 6

For the bad method of sit-ups shown above, work out with your partner the reason why it is a bad exercise. Then describe what makes the other method a good alternative.

Key terms

- **contra-indicated**
- **high impact**
- **hyperextension**
- **hyperflexion**

Safety aspects and risk assessment in sport and physical activity

Risk assessment – prevention of injuries

After taking up a sport and training to improve our skills and fitness levels with the aim of playing at a good level of performance, it is important to assess the potential risks of your chosen activity. This means knowing what the risks may be in your activity and how to avoid or minimize them. You should always act to minimize the risk of injury to yourself or to an opponent or team member.

All sports or activities where competition is part of the game have rules to protect the players and those associated with the organization, including the spectators or supporters.

In both competitive sports and those where people take part just for the pleasure of being involved there are rules for the safety of the participants and others.

Two examples might be:
- *football* – players wear protective clothing to help prevent or reduce the risk or severity of injury
- *golf* – if players hit the ball and see it flying in the direction of someone else, they shout 'Fore!' to alert the person and to prevent injury.

Unfortunately, we now see practices that take place outside the rules and morals of the game, even at the highest level, where an injury might ruin a player's career. Players can now be banned or heavily fined for over-aggressive play outside the rules and the 'spirit of the game'.

Protective clothing

Many sports call for protective sportswear. Some sports have this safety feature built into

the rules, football and hockey being two such games. The clothing often varies according to position – hockey goalkeepers wear much more protective sportswear than the rest of the team.

It is also important not to wear clothing that might injure an opponent, or indeed a team-mate. Jewellery, for example, should always be removed before playing, or taped over if it cannot be removed.

Task 1

Work with a partner to produce a list of four sports with their appropriate clothing and equipment. Try to pick your sports from different categories, e.g. team contact sports; individual contact sports; racket games; individual non-contact sports. Record the information in a table.

Hockey goalkeepers probably wear more protective sportswear than players in any other sport

Triple jump champion Ashia Hansen wears heel cups to absorb the shock as the heel lands

Appropriate footwear

One of the main aspects of sports clothing is footwear. It's not only that you can play an activity better with the correct footwear – it is also safer. In contact invasion games it is easy to see why this is so, but in athletics the runners need spikes which help them to run faster. However, these can also be dangerous and injuries often happen to athletes who get spiked either by themselves or by other athletes. Jumpers, especially triple jumpers, wear special heel cups to protect their heel, especially when they land from the hop but also in the step phase of the movement.

However, it is the road runners and marathon runners who have to take very special care with their footwear. Pounding the roads takes its toll on the feet, ankles, knees and hip joints, as well as the muscles in the legs, most especially the gastrocnemius. Shoes are the most important part of their equipment and must be chosen very carefully, especially as it is estimated that each foot lands approximately 800 times per running mile!

Running shoes are very expensive as much research goes into their manufacture. Choosing the right shoe is very important and it is not only comfort but also support that needs to be taken into account. Some runners pronate, which means their feet turn inwards as they touch the ground, and this can cause injuries to the shins and the knees. It is also possible to get special inserts to go inside running shoes, which give extra protection. Specialist shoes exist for many different sporting activities.

Tracksuits

Safety in training is as important as safety in competition. Experienced sportspeople include a good tracksuit in their training and preparation clothing. Tracksuits keep the body warm and this increases flexibility, which helps prevent injury while training or warming up, and when cooling down.

Weight training

There are a number of useful items of equipment to have in your training bag when attending a weights session. Again, shoes are important and good tennis, aerobics or training shoes would be advised. Other items would include a lifting belt, but your school or your training club might well supply this. This will help to support your back but should not be an excuse for poor lifting technique. Some people also use weight training gloves. These are not necessary when using a multi-gym but are useful when doing free weights.

Task 2

Name an activity of your choice and write a list of the equipment you would need for a typical training session.

Key terms

● **assess**
● **contact sports**
● **non-contact sports**
● **rules**
● **spirit of the game**

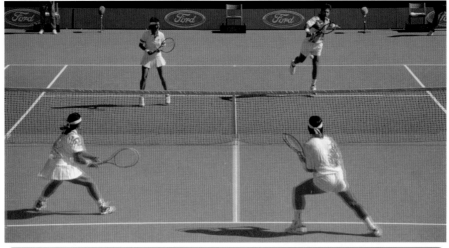

In tennis, women and men can compete in mixed teams

Balanced competition

Another way to make sport safe is to try to level the competition by grading competitors in various ways. Golf operates a handicap system, but this has nothing to do with safety, only with competition. The main sports that grade skills with regard to safety are the combat sports, such as karate and judo.

Weight categories

Karate and judo have clear skill levels and players take part according to their abilities, while in professional sports such as boxing, the competitors are categorized by weight. As we have seen already (page 45), this can cause other problems when fighters try to make the weight and become dehydrated. Weight lifting is also divided into weight divisions, but this is again mainly to equalize the competition and not for safety reasons.

Mixed or single sex competition

Most sports have single sex competition only, though there are some where men and women compete in mixed teams and a few in which they compete in open competition. Athletics and swimming are clearly divided by sex, though again not necessarily for reasons of safety. Those divided in such a way are the contact sports, though mixed hockey is very popular.

Task 3

Explain why it might be more important in a combat sport such as judo, to compete in grades divided according to skill rather than weight.

Age groups

Sports competition among young children has for some time been quite a controversial issue. Some people think there is too much competition at an early age. In terms of safety, overuse injuries are frequent. Although age-graded competitions within the school programme are common, children do often compete outside their age group, especially if they are very talented. Although the age restriction is clearly an issue of even competition and safety, the situation often arises when two competitors in the same age band are a mismatch in terms of height and weight. Is this therefore the safest way to group children in competition?

Task 4

Discuss with a partner the age group debate regarding competition between similarly aged children with a clear discrepancy in height and weight.

Sometimes competitors in the same age band are clearly mismatched

Sports injuries

It is in the nature of sport that however well players and competitors are protected, however well prepared and however well the competition or game has been organized, at some time injuries will happen.

A sports physiotherapist attached to a team, in the football Premiership, for example, pays much more attention to the players than to the game. When a hard tackle takes place they observe the outcome to the player rather than what happens to the ball. From what they observe (see pages 10–11) when an injury occurs they will already have a good knowledge of what has happened because of the way it came about. If a player is injured because they have been kicked, it is likely to be one type of injury. If they twist at a joint it will be another type of injury.

Joint injuries

One of the most common injuries in sport is the twisted ankle, often in invasion games such as hockey, football and rugby. We have looked at the ankle joint and so we know that it has ligaments, which attach the bones of the ankle together, and tendons, which further strengthen the ankle. A twisted ankle means that the foot has turned too far inwards, resulting in the fibres tearing loose from where they are attached.

Dislocations

These often happen as a result of a hard blow which causes one of the bones at a joint to be displaced. The most apparent sign will be the deformity at the joint, with the joint locked in position. The player will not be able to move the injured part and there is likely to be swelling. The player will be in severe pain at or near the joint. There may also be a fracture of one of the bones and if there is any doubt the injury should be treated as a fracture.

Torn cartilage

This can often happen when a player is pivoting on one foot. The player will usually fall to the ground and suffer pain on the inside of the knee. It is also likely that they will not be able to straighten the knee joint.

The immediate treatment for both of these injuries would be to follow the **RICE** principle:

1 **R**est (i.e. stop playing)
2 apply **I**ce or cold pack
3 apply **C**ompression and
4 **E**levate the injury.

Definitions

signs	what you can see, what you can feel, what you may hear or what you can smell
symptoms	what the player feels and conveys to you

Key terms

- balanced competition
- dislocate
- observation
- physiotherapist
- Rest, Ice, Compression, Elevate
- signs and symptoms
- torn cartilage

Tennis and golf elbow

Both of these conditions are tendon injuries caused by overuse, and tennis elbow may be caused by using a racket with a handle that is the wrong size. The symptom of tennis elbow is pain on the outside of the elbow, while golfer's elbow gives pain on the inside. The treatment for both is RICE, but if it persists medical help is advised.

Muscle/soft tissue injuries

Muscle tears, pulled muscles and strained muscles are terms often used for what is basically the same type of common injury in which the small fibres are torn away from their attachment to a tendon. These fibres shorten during muscle contraction and then lengthen when the muscle relaxes, when the muscle is used antagonistically. During intense competition they have to contract and relax very quickly, and this can cause the connective tissue and the blood vessels that run inside them to be torn.

Many sportspeople have strong, very well developed quadriceps (remember the kicking muscle) because the nature of invasion games is such that they get plenty of exercise, but the hamstrings (the sprinter's muscles) are often pulled and for this reason they need to be given special attention when warming up.

As for joint injuries, use RICE when muscles are injured:

1 **R**est – stop playing or training
2 **I**ce – a bag of peas from the freezer, cold water or ice cubes, but this can damage the skin and should not be used for too long
3 **C**ompression – using pressure to hold the ice pack on the injury
4 **E**levation – raise the injury and keep it that way for 24 hours.

Fractures

A fracture is a broken or cracked bone. Thankfully they are relatively uncommon injuries in sport, when compared with the number of players involved from week to week. Fractures can occur from a blow, to the tibia for example, but the fibula is often broken by a severe twisting or wrenching of the ankle joint.

A sign of a fracture might be the noise of the bone as it breaks and the symptoms will include pain at the site of the injury and, if the injured part is a limb, an inability to move it. The point of injury will be very tender and swelling might occur with bruising later. Another obvious symptom might be deformity at the point of the break – the clavicle is a good example.

There are two main types of fracture:

- *open* – when the broken bones protrudes through the skin and bleeding may also be present, and of course there is the danger of infection
- *closed* – when the skin over the break is not broken.

There are other types of fractures, including a greenstick fracture, which is only part way across the bone. This is common at the wrist joint, as pointed out earlier with regard to running in the gym and using the walls to turn against.

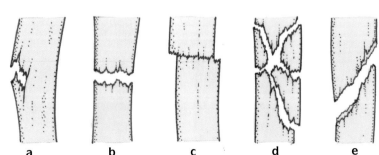

a **greenstick** – break only part way across the bone
b **transverse** – break straight across
c **impacted** – pieces locked into each other
d **comminuted** – broken into more than two pieces
e **oblique** – break at an angle

Types of fracture. Fractures can also be *open* or *closed*, depending on whether the skin is broken or intact

Skin damage

Cuts

We know that blood is required to carry oxygen and food in the form of glucose around the body to the tissues, and to remove waste products via the circulatory system. Cuts are open wounds which allow blood to escape from the body and their importance depends on how severe they are. The signs are obvious in the case of external bleeding but a symptom would be if the player also felt pain at the site of the injury.

Pressure on the wound will help to stem the blood flow, but a clean dressing should be used. An open cut may require the edges of the wound to be squeezed together. As infection can be passed on through open wounds, both to the patient and from the patient, special gloves are worn when giving treatment. Alternatively, the player might put pressure on the wound themselves, or draw the edges of the open wound together. If the wound is to a limb, raise and support it. A sterile dressing and padding can then be used.

Grazes

Grazes appear when the top layers of skin are scraped off an area and the signs are again obvious. The symptom will be pain at the site of the injury. In a sports situation these wounds often contain grit or dirt which needs to be cleaned out to avoid infection. Friction burns are similar wounds and should be treated in the same way, with a clean sterile dressing.

Blisters

Blisters are thin bubbles that can occur from poorly fitting shoes or boots as a result of friction. The blister forms a protection while new skin is growing below the serum that has leaked into it.

The outer layer of the blister will eventually peel off and the blister should never be broken because of the risk of infection.

Bruises

Bruises are wounds that bleed internally, which accounts for their dark blue colour. They are often caused by blows, or by twisting joints, which breaks the tiny blood vessels.

These types of skin damage injury are very common in many sports, and some such as boxing have specialized people on hand to deal with the situation. Abrasions caused by training indoors for outdoor sports, and using some all-weather areas, accounts for many slight cuts and grazes.

Boxing has 'seconds' to deal with skin injuries

Task 1

Name the serious condition that can be passed on by blood contact through open sores or wounds, which emphasizes the importance of special care and the need to wear surgical gloves when dealing with open wounds.

Key terms

- closed fracture
- greenstick fracture
- open fracture
- sterile dressing

Hypothermia

Body fat has been mentioned earlier and we noted its importance to the body in terms of conserving heat. Remember, those of us who have more body fat feel the cold less. We also noted that warm clothing is important for getting warm before taking part in an activity.

Hypothermia is a condition that occurs when our body temperature falls below about 35°C (95°F). If it falls below 26°C, recovery is unlikely. It often occurs when people are exposed to extreme cold, on mountains, in water or in cold, often snowy conditions. In such conditions added complications like tiredness, hunger, lack of fitness and **dehydration** impact on the situation.

The symptoms are not always easy to recognize but shivering is common, and the skin will be cold and pale. A check should be made on the person's temperature. The pulse rate may be slower than normal and they may behave irrationally and eventually become unconscious.

To treat the condition, remember that it is the core temperature that needs to be raised, so wet clothing needs to be removed and replaced with warm clothing. Where possible the re-warming should come from the core of the body, not from the outside in, as this could cause a drop in blood pressure. A bath at a bearable temperature not exceeding 40°C, hot drinks and high-energy food such as chocolate to give quick energy will help. Those suffering from hypothermia should be re-warmed gradually if they got cold gradually, but if, for example, they have fallen into the cold sea, they can be re-warmed more quickly.

Dehydration

Water is almost as important as oxygen for the body, and athletes and games players need to replenish any that is lost through sweat, urine and in the water vapour that is breathed out with each breath. In some sports this loss may come about naturally, simply by training or competing, but in others it may be forced, perhaps by wearing extra clothing, such as tracksuits or sweatsuits, or even as we have seen, by taking certain types of drugs (diuretics). During excessive sweat loss the body loses electrolytes (see page 48) and fluids and both must be replaced if athletes are to avoid dehydration. This condition can lead to liver **glycogen** deficiency and, in turn, low blood **glucose** levels and a minimal amount of glycogen in the muscles. The results of this will be extreme tiredness, **nausea** and perhaps even dizziness. Not the best way either to train or compete. A good reason to replace water and electrolytes regularly!

Task 2

Find the name of a sports drink and check the label to see what it contains. Make a list from the label. Does it contain electrolytes?

Long-distance swimmers use grease to keep out the cold

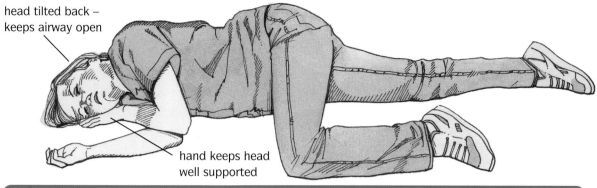

head tilted back –
keeps airway open

hand keeps head
well supported

The recovery position

Unconsciousness

There are many causes that can render a person unconscious, but within a sporting context the most common are probably a head injury, fainting, heart attack, stroke, **asphyxia** and shock. However epilepsy and diabetes, which are not directly concerned with sport, can also bring about this situation.

The mnemonic (memory aid) **D.R.A.B.C.** will help to remind you of the stages to follow if a person is found to be unconscious.

D   is for *Danger* – referring to both the injured person and the rescuer, and it is important to take this into account.

R   is for *Response* – how the person responds, for example to you asking a question. Clues might be gained from their eyes, movement and speech. If the casualty is unresponsive, shout or send for help.

A   is for *Airway* – is it clear for them to breathe?

B   is for *Breathing* –
   ● look to see if the chest rises
   ● listen at the mouth
   ● feel the chest to check if it rises.

C   is for *Circulation* – check the pulse.

If a person is unconscious but breathing on their own, they should be turned or put into the recovery position (see the picture above).

In this position they are unlikely to swallow their vomit if they are sick. In some contact sports a player might sometimes swallow their tongue and so block the airway. Putting them into the recovery position will ensure that the airway remains unblocked.

Concussion

This is an injury to the brain which can be caused in sport from a blow to the head or the jaw, or from a fall on the head. Signs might be that the player becomes unconscious, has shallow breathing and a pale face. They may be cold and their pulse might race. They may vomit or not remember what happened to them. In a game they may not know what the score is, who the opponents are or where they are playing. Even if the player has apparently recovered, professional medical help should be found.

Task 3

Work with a partner and practise putting each other into the recovery position.

Key terms

● blood glucose level
● body temperature
● concussion
● dehydration
● D.R.A.B.C.
● electrolytes
● glycogen
● hypothermia
● nausea
● unconsciousness

Posture

One of the functions of muscle tone is that it keeps the body primed and ready for instant action. The second reason is that it keeps the body in an upright position, without us even thinking about it. This is called posture. Imagine what would happen if all our muscles relaxed at the same time. Our body would collapse. So our joints are held firm by the flexor and extensor muscles both working at the same time (see page 120).

Bad posture

It is important to keep our bodies balanced, but often we allow our bodies to stoop or sag. When this happens our weight becomes unevenly distributed and some muscles are required to carry extra weight, and if they are weak they soon become tired.

Many people suffer from lower back pain at some time in their life, and there may be causes for this. Continual bad posture is one of them and it can lead to long-term deformity of the spinal column.

In today's society, working for long hours slouched over a desk or sitting in front of a computer screen can add to the problem.

This man has a classic case of bad posture!

Poorly fitting shoes, and especially shoes with high heels, move the body, especially the spinal column, out of its normal position.

Poor muscle tone, poor flexibility and weak muscles in the lower back, legs and the abdominal muscles all add up to poor posture. Add to this the fact that many people are overweight – another contributory reason for bad posture.

Task 4

Look at the photograph at the bottom left. Describe all the things that this illustrates about bad posture.

Curvature of the spine

Lordosis

This condition causes lower back problems, leading to pain and makes it difficult to jump with a straight spinal column. Weak abdominals and gluteus maximus muscles can add to these problems.

Kyfosis

Sometimes described as 'hump back', this is an excessive outwards curvature or flexion in the upper back. This is often due to weak adductor muscles in the shoulder region.

Scoliosis

This is a condition in which there is lateral (sideways) curvature of the spine, which can be observed with an X-ray.

Lifting

It is important to adopt a safe posture when lifting, e.g. weights in weight training or heavy objects such as boxes and parcels. Lift with the legs where possible, keep the back straight and the weight close to your body.

Good posture

If a person has good posture they will stand upright with very little effort. The head will be well balanced over the shoulders, the spinal column will be straight above the hips, knees will be straight and feet square on the ground. The whole body will look and feel balanced. Even when in different positions such as sitting down, walking or running, the position will look elegant, balanced and comfortable.

Task 5

Look at the two photographs on these pages and compare the postures.

Supermodels always have excellent posture

Improving or maintaining good posture

In the earlier parts of the book we investigated the reasons for taking part in physical activity (pages 30–3). The very first two we looked at were 'improves body shape' and 'helps the individual to look and feel good'.

Improving or maintaining a good posture must be involved with this. So how do we do it?

Aerobic and anaerobic exercise takes care of the heart, lungs, blood and the blood vessels, while strength work, be it strength exercises or weight training, improves muscular strength and muscle tone – and it is these latter two which in turn improve posture. To improve in this department, heavy weights are not needed and in many respects it is the discipline of lifting correctly which assists the person to achieve and maintain good posture. Finally, we need flexibility – the all too often forgotten aspect of fitness – which, when combined with the above work, will help to produce an athlete or individual with improved body shape who both looks and feels good.

Task 6

Give a very brief outline of the type of weights programme you think would help to produce good posture.

Key terms

- balance
- flexibility
- muscle tone
- posture
- spinal column

Skill related fitness

Motor skills

Earlier in the book (pages 34–7) when we investigated the factors affecting participation and performance, motor skills were listed as one important factor. These involve:

A for *Agility*

B for *Balance*

C for *Co-ordination*

P for *Power*

R for *Reaction-time*

S for *Speed*

These skills are different from the health and fitness factors and should not be mixed up with them. We have covered a lot of ground in investigating and learning about fitness. We have then tried to develop this through training, building upon what we may have been given as natural ability – body build being a simple example.

Having good motor skills may help us to become fitter, and certainly helps us to become good at sport, but as with the fitness factors, they can be developed and improved. Different sports may need more of one motor skill than another, though many need a mix.

Task 1

Make a list of the sports activities you are personally doing for your own practical coursework. Then next to each activity add the skill you think it is most concerned with.

Body type

Being a certain somatotype may influence our sporting abilities, for example, the endomorphic sumo wrestler or the ectomorphic long distance runner. But some sports are very much more dominant in terms of skill and in these sports we may find many different body types.

Even in football, players of quite different body shapes can be successful due to their different specialist skills – for example Michael Owen (speed), Emile Heskey (power) and David Seaman (agility).

Task 2

Choose a well-known sport in which you think skill is the most important factor. Write down the names of three well-known players of different builds who excel in that sport. If the sport has special positions that require different skills, describe these positions and skills.

A is for agility

| agility | Charles Corbin defines this as: 'the ability to change the position of the body quickly and to control the movement of your whole body'. |

Gymnastics floorwork, flic-flacs and/or a back somersault are good examples of activities for which agility is a major priority.

At the highest levels, gymnastics requires great agility

B is for balance

balance	The specification defines this as: 'the ability to retain the centre of mass (gravity) of the body above the base of support with reference to **static** – stationary – or **dynamic** – changing – conditions of movement, shape and orientation'.

In a sports context, this can mean balance while at rest but it can also mean balance whilst on the move. In considering balance in certain sports this needs to be noted and explained. When we looked at agility in gymnastics, the examples were floorwork and flic-flacs or back somersaults. With balance on the beam, examples could be in the context of holding a balanced position, e.g. handstand (static balance), or keeping balanced while on the move, e.g. a walk-over (dynamic balance). Static balance is most important in shooting-type activities such as archery or pistol shooting.

Task 3

For one of your sports, give an example of a static balance. For the same sport or another one, give an example of a dynamic balance.

This position is an example of static balance

Movements on the beam require dynamic balance

C is for co-ordination

co-ordination	The specification defines this as: 'the ability to use two or more body parts together'.

Just as there are different types of balance, so too are there different types of co-ordination. The racket games require good hand-eye co-ordination in order to strike the ball or shuttle correctly. In football there are perhaps three specific types of co-ordination:

- *hand-eye co-ordination* – for the goalkeeper to catch or punch the ball when it is crossed (often under the pressure of opposing forwards)
- *foot-eye co-ordination* – needed to strike the ball to pass, shoot or control it
- *head-eye co-ordination* – needed to strike the ball with the head in order to clear a centre or to aim at the target to score.

Most people tend to be better co-ordinated on one side of their body, i.e. they are better with their right hand than their left, or better with their right foot than their left. Generally, if you are right-handed you will be right footed, but not always. Some people may be right-handed and naturally left-footed, or in some sports, such as cricket, they may bat right-handed and bowl left-handed.

Task 4

Write down the names of two of your sports and then describe a situation where co-ordination is needed such as (but not the same as) the ones stated above.

Key terms

- agility
- co-ordination
- dynamic balance
- static balance

P is for power

power	The specification defines this as: 'the ability to do strength performances quickly power = strength × speed'.

As implied in the definition, an increase in your strength or an increase in your speed will result in an increase in your power. In sport we may use power to propel ourselves and/or to propel an object. Sprinters need to be powerful in order to drive their bodies out of the blocks when the gun fires. Just being strong will not enable you to do this – you also need speed.

Throwers need to be powerful, but strength alone is not enough. In football there is the long 'throw in' which needs strength and speed, and in many sports players need to be able to jump high, either in a game or in the high jump or pole vault in athletics. Long jump and triple jump, although they are horizontal jumps, are both activities that also require power.

When we looked at constructing a weight training schedule (pages 102–3) we examined a number of variables. Number 6 for example dealt with how fast the exercise should be done. In order to gain power, speed in the lift is important with the recovery or lowering of the weight being slower. Free weights are probably better than a multi-gym for improving power.

Task 5

Give an example from one of your sports of a situation where power is required.

R is for reaction time

reaction time	The specification defines this as: 'the time between the presentation of a **stimulus** and the onset of movement'.

The trigger is pulled, the gun fires, the athletes start to run – the time in between is known as reaction time. This is the example that most people would recognize, but there are many other examples too. For sprinters or swimmers, it is the time taken for them to hear the stimulus (sound) but not so for the timekeepers. The gun fires, the smoke appears, the timekeepers start their watches, so for them the stimulus is the sight of the smoke, not the sound of the gun which acts as the stimulus.

A sight stimulus is the signal for a reaction in most sports where reactions are involved other than the starting of a race. A ball or shuttle is struck by a racket and the receiver has to react to the sight. It is possible to improve reactions by practice or anticipation from experience of playing the game.

Task 6

Once again, after naming one of your activities, give an example of a situation when it is important to have fast reactions. Do not use the examples already given.

These runners are reacting to an audible stimulus while the timekeepers react to a visible stimulus – the smoke from the gun

S is for speed

speed	The specification defines this as: 'the differential rate an individual is able to perform a movement or cover a distance in a short period of time'.

This includes speed of leg (e.g. Michael Owen), speed of limbs and speed of thought (e.g. Prince Naseem). If a sportsperson could choose one natural ability out of all the skills needed to become a champion, this is probably the one they would choose. There may be sports where lack of it can be overcome, but it is an essential ingredient for most champions in sport and it can sometimes make up for a lack of other skills.

Speed can be improved by practice (e.g. sprinters practise fast leg and arm movements when running on the spot).

Task 7

Name one of your sports and give an example, other than running, of when speed is important.

The speed of the club head on impact with the ball is important in golf

Task 8

Work with a partner to devise a practice for each of the motor skills. This should not be a test. After devising each practice try it out on another pair and let them try out their practice on you. Discuss and compare the success of each practice.

Task 9

Choose and write down the name of a skill from each of the two groups set out below:

agility	balance
power	co-ordination
speed	reaction time

Devise a test for each of the skills you have chosen.

Motor skills in everyday life

We have seen that improved fitness can help us to perform more efficiently in our normal daily activities, be they in work or in our leisure. Now we have seen that the same applies to motor skills – for example, having a good reaction time is useful when driving a motor car.

Task 10

For each of the skill-related fitnesses on pages 144–7, give an example of when each is valuable or helpful in our normal daily lives outside the sporting situation.

Key terms

- power
- practice
- reaction time
- speed

Drugs in sport

We have looked at a variety of abilities which sportspeople may be gifted with, develop and/or train for. But there is something else that some athletes use to help them to win and that is drugs.

Range of drugs

The all-embracing word 'drugs' covers a wide range of substances. Some of these are used on a regular basis by many of us. The obvious ones are caffeine, which we take in tea and coffee, nicotine, which people use in smoking, and ethanol, more commonly known as alcohol.

Socially acceptable drugs

There are other drugs that we use on a less frequent basis. The doctor may prescribe these and we get them from the pharmacist and call them medicines – paracetamol and aspirin are among the most common. These drugs could be described as socially acceptable, because as long as you are of a certain age, they are not illegal.

Task 1

Write down the name of any medicine that you can remember that you or a member of your family take or have taken.

Socially unacceptable drugs

There are also drugs that come under the term socially unacceptable, and these are illegal. This group includes heroin, cocaine, LSD, amphetamines, barbiturates, cannabis and ecstasy.

Performance-enhancing drugs

There is a third category: the performance-enhancing drugs. This group includes some of the socially acceptable drugs, and many of the illegal drugs.

Task 2

Work with a partner to find your own definition of the word 'drug'. Make sure that it can be applied to all the different categories.

What is a drug?

One definition suggests that a drug is a substance that can be taken in a variety of ways to produce expected and welcome physical and/or **psychological** effects on the person taking it. It may also cause some effects that are both unpleasant and unwanted. These are known as side effects.

Side effects

One of the side effects of drugs is that they can become addictive, and this is as true of both nicotine and alcohol as it is of heroin and cocaine. As well as being addictive, and very difficult for some people to quit, smoking can cause other physical problems.

Contrary to general belief, coronary heart disease (CHD), not cancer, is the most common cause of death attributed to smoking. Smoking damages the heart and the oxygen-carrying capability of the blood. It also damages the blood vessels and raises your blood pressure.

Apart from all the health risks, smoking will also reduce your ability to perform well in sport

Smoking one cigarette can raise the pulse rate, and operations take on a higher risk if you smoke. The good news is that stopping smoking lessens these risks which are considerably better after one year of non-smoking!

However, nicotine is not a banned drug. Alcohol, on the other hand, *is* banned in some sports where it may be used as a sedative (having a calming effect), e.g. shooting or archery, or where it is considered a safety risk – in motor sports, for example, where it will slow down reaction time and decrease judgement.

Both alcohol and caffeine cause extra urine to be disposed of and therefore add to the risk of dehydration, while the long-term effects of alcohol include liver damage known as cirrhosis. This is the reason George Best had a liver transplant in 2002.

While not a banned drug in football, alcohol is used as a recreational drug and alcoholism is a major concern to the Football Association, especially in view of the disclosures regarding both Paul Merson when at Arsenal and Paul Gascoigne when at Middlesborough.

Task 3

Name three different sports stars implicated in taking drugs in order to enhance their sporting performance.

The 1998 Tour de France was brought to a halt by protests following drug testing

Why take drugs?

It has been shown over a long period of time that sportspeople decide themselves to take drugs to enhance or improve their performance, or are encouraged to do so by their coach or fellow athletes.

In recent years it has been proved or alleged that there has been drug-taking by sportspeople in, among other sports, cycling (the 1998 Tour de France), swimming, association football, rugby, athletics, tennis, snooker, weight lifting, American football, basketball, skiing and also by contestants in the World's Strongest Man competition.

The temptation is great with such high stakes – it is said that winning an Olympic gold medal in some sports is worth a million dollars in endorsements.

Even on a day-to-day basis sportspeople make a lot of money by simply competing at the highest levels. Even if they do not win, drugs may allow a lesser athlete to take part in their sport at a level they could not otherwise have reached. Another incentive is that a professional sportsperson's active money-spinning days are comparatively few, and they must make enough money and/or have a big enough name to enable them to live well after their competition days are over.

Task 4

For the three stars you named in the previous task, state why you think they took drugs.

Key terms

- alcohol
- **performance-enhancing drugs**
- side effects
- smoking
- **socially acceptable drugs**
- **socially unacceptable drugs**

Performance-enhancing drugs

Performance-enhancing drugs fall into two categories:

- prohibited classes of substances
- prohibited methods.

(IOC Medical Code, 31/1/98)

Prohibited classes of substances

In this category there are five groups of drugs that are used to produce different effects:

- stimulants
- narcotics/analgesics
- anabolic agents
- diuretics
- peptide, chemical and physical manipulation.

Stimulants

Stimulants are the second most common drug used by sportspeople, and they include amphetamines, ephedrine and cocaine (which are sometimes found in medicines for colds and pain relief), as well as nicotine and caffeine. The latter two drugs, as we have seen, are very

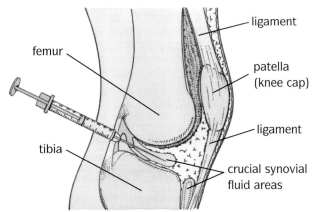

femur

ligament

patella (knee cap)

ligament

tibia

crucial synovial fluid areas

❶ Synovial fluid is secreted in knee joint to provide natural lubrication and elasticity between bones.

❷ After injury, its effect can be lessened allowing bone surfaces to grate against each other painfully.

❸ New treatment injects liquid into joint which acts just like original natural fluid.

This diagram details a new treatment for knee injuries, which may reduce the temptation to use narcotics or analgesics

common and many people take them regularly. These drugs help to make people more alert, enabling them to think more quickly by stimulating the central nervous system (CNS). Using these drugs helps to overcome tiredness and they are especially useful to offset the effects of lactic acid in the muscles.

Cocaine is a recreational drug used by many professional sportspeople, including American footballers, baseball players and boxers. In football, Paul Merson admitted to being a cocaine addict.

Stimulants may produce side effects such as insomnia, irritability, irregular heartbeat, increased heart rate and high blood pressure, and some, such as amphetamines, are highly addictive.

Narcotics/analgesics

Injuries are a fear and a problem for many sportspeople. They want to compete, not sit and watch from the sidelines, and many of them make poor spectators, especially in front of their own team-mates. As a result, many are prepared to take drugs to get back into the action as quickly as possible. This is the category of drug that helps them to do this and includes such things as heroin, methadone, pethidine and the powerful painkiller, morphine. Morphine is a very powerful drug and can effect the emotions and cause hallucinations.

These drugs act by depressing the CNS. These give relief from painful injuries, but by allowing the injured player to take part the risk of severe or long lasting injury is increased. This is why they are banned and also because the side effects, such as loss of concentration, balance and co-ordination, are not the responses that a sportsperson would want.

Task 5

Can you think of one incident reported in the media when a player was given an injection to allow them to take part in their sport?

Anabolic steroids

Anabolic steroids are reputed to be the most common drugs used to enhance performance in sport. These drugs mimic the male hormone testosterone. For this reason they have the effect of deepening the voice and causing the growth of facial hair, side effects that of course are most notable when they occur in women! The positive effect for which they are taken is to increase muscle mass and develop bone growth, and therefore increase strength, while at the same time allowing the athlete to train harder. The other added attraction is that they produce results quickly. Some people believe that the same effects can be gained legally by using good training methods and correct nutrition.

Another effect upon the performer is to increase aggression. Some may take it more for this reason than for muscle building, though the drug is normally used to prevent muscle wastage and as an aid to rehabilitation.

Among the best known of these drugs are testosterone, stanozonol, nandrolone and bodlenone. The side effects of these drugs include mood swings and aggression, as well as anxiety. The face can become round and puffy

and heart attacks, strokes and high blood pressure can occur. There is also an increased risk of muscle injuries and liver disease can result, as well as infertility in women. At their worst they can cause death!

Task 6

Think of three quite different sports in which you think the development of muscle through taking steroids would be a strong temptation.

Diuretics

Diuretics are used to increase the amount of urine produced and to increase kidney function, thereby speeding up the elimination of fluid from the body. In turn this will cause rapid weight loss in sports where performers are required to compete within strict weight boundaries.

The side effects of diuretics are dehydration, which can result in dizziness, muscle cramps, headaches and nausea. The long-term effects are kidney problems.

Another reason why such drugs are taken is to reduce the concentration of any other banned substances that may be present in the athlete's urine sample.

Task 7

Write down the names of three sports in which the participants might be tempted to use diuretics to lose weight quickly.

Steroids are a strong temptation in sports that require strength and aggression

Key terms

- **anabolic steroids**
- **central nervous system (CNS)**
- **diuretics**
- **narcotics/analgesics**
- **stimulants**
- **testosterone**

Peptide, chemical and physical manipulation

These types of drug are often used to produce the same effects as anabolic steroids, namely, to increase muscle growth, to assist in recovery from injury and heavy training sessions, and to increase the number of red blood cells to carry extra oxygen.

We all produce hormones naturally but they can also be produced synthetically and high doses are sometimes taken by athletes to increase muscle development. Human growth hormone (hGH) is now used by some athletes for this reason. Athletes are tested at regular intervals to check for the use of steroids, but human growth hormone, a comparatively new drug, is now used to gain the same advantage. There are also thought to be fewer side effects than steroids. Although there is no urine test for hGH, it can be detected through a blood test, but as yet this is not an accepted test and was not used at the Sydney Olympics of 2000.

Erythropoietin (EPO) is used to treat people with anaemia as it increases the production of the red blood cells, therefore it increases the amount of haemoglobin available to take up oxygen. This in turn increases aerobic capacity.

One of the problems with EPO is that it thickens the blood, a condition which also occurs in athletes who have competed too much, because of dehydration. The result is that it is much more difficult for blood to pass through the small capillaries and there is a risk of a heart attack or stroke.

However, although EPO is not detectable through a urine text, a blood test for EPO was introduced at the Sydney Olympics.

Prohibited methods

Blood doping (see page 77) is a banned process, not a banned drug. It has been known for many years that if an athlete trains at high altitude the oxygen-carrying capacity of their blood increases. Because of this fact, athletes born at high altitude have had a distinct advantage in the endurance events. Therefore it has become a recognized practice for athletes to train at high altitude for a period of time, and then to have as much as two pints of blood taken from their body and the red blood cells frozen. The body's system quickly recovers and the normal eight pints of blood is restored. Near a competition day, the red blood cells are put back into the athlete's blood stream and this process is thought to increase their performance by as much as 20%. Only in certain circumstances can this process be detected.

Task 8

Give an example of an event in which it would be an advantage to use blood doping.

Lasse Viren, Olympic 5000m champion in 1972, was suspected of using blood doping

The laws and the enforcers!

The International Olympic Committee (IOC) who run the Olympic Games have strict rules on prohibited (banned) substances. In fact there are over 4000 of them!

The IOC take random tests of athletes, both in their season and out of it, by taking a urine sample. This sample is then split into two smaller samples and a test is carried out on the first of these and checked against a database. Any drugs that may be found are investigated further. If any drug is then found to be present, the second urine sample is checked with the athlete present.

The taking of substances to improve performance goes back a long way. It was reported that the USSR used androgenic anabolic steroids (testosterone) by injection to improve the performance of their weight lifters in 1952. The USA followed suit.

It was not until the 1970s that the governing bodies began to make it illegal to take these substances and testing began. The IOC first enforced a full-scale testing programme for the 1972 Olympics Games in Munich, but it was 1975 before they first banned anabolic steroids.

In February 1999, at a conference in Lausanne, the IOC wanted agreement on two specific points:

1   a single international anti-doping agency
2   a blanket two-year ban for competitors found guilty of drug-taking.

The governing bodies of cycling, tennis and football would not agree to the two-year ban, but insisted on the inclusion of the words 'specific, exceptional circumstances'.

The position is further complicated by the fact that although there is a blood test there is no urine test for EPO, and another muscle-building substance, creatine, is widely used in sport but is not on the banned list.

In some countries the testing procedures are not as strict as in others, and some sports governing bodies do not include certain drugs on their banned list. For example, Mark McGwire, who broke the home run record in the American Baseball League, admits to taking the muscle-building drug, androstenedione (andro), which is banned by the IOC, but not in major league baseball.

When athletes test positive there are ways to prove innocence, or in some cases to avoid being found guilty. Ben Johnson, now famous for being found guilty of taking stanozonol, blamed the positive test on the medication he took to treat his stammer. Butch Reynolds, the American 400 metres runner, claimed that his sample had been mixed up with that of a guilty East German.

What does it take to be a champion in sport?

When the French baron Pierre de Coubertin revived the modern Olympic Games, he could not have envisaged the levels to which athletes would go to win a gold medal.

Taking performance-enhancing drugs is regarded as cheating and athletes found guilty pay the ultimate penalty within their sport – they are banned. In life it may be even worse, Jon Borg Simonsen (age 32) the World's Strongest Man, and American Footballer, Lyle Alzado are but two who paid the ultimate price!

Key terms

- blood doping
- chemical manipulation
- International Olympic Committee (IOC)
- physical manipulation

Revision

Before you start your revision, make sure you know exactly which Edexcel specification you are taking. If you are taking the short course, only revise what you need to do.

Getting a list of revision topics

It will help you revise if you make a list of topics for revision using the unit headings that appear in the student book. Then tick them off the list when you think you have covered that topic. Remember to come back to any you are not sure of, or that you found difficult. You could make your list and then revise using some of the ideas below.

Definitions

Make a list of definitions of key terms and get a partner to read them out in random order. First of all, you should say what term is being defined. For example, if you are told that the definition is 'extremely overweight', your answer would be that this is the definition for the key term 'obese'.

Next, get your partner to read out key terms and you supply the definitions for them. For example, if you were asked to define the term 'fitness', what would your answer be?

You should be familiar with all the key terms, but the following list of terms is particularly important and you should make sure you know their definitions:

- health, exercise, fitness and performance
- health-related exercise terms
- skill fitness terms
- cardiac output, stroke volume, heart rate
- vital capacity, tidal volume
- overweight, overfat, obese.

Things you need to learn

There are some topics that will be best to learn by heart. A good way of doing this is to read about them in the student book and then close the book and write down the key points of what you have read. Then check what you have written against the student book. There are also some good ways to help you remember facts. For example, when learning about safety, remember that 'Dr ABC and RICE' is not a firm of solicitors! Each of those letters represents a word – Danger, Response, Airway, Breathing, Circulation for D.R.A.B.C., and Rest, Ice, Compression, Elevate for RICE. Each letter will help you to remember the word; the order that the words come in should be easy if you remember D.R.A.B.C. and RICE. There are many other points that you can bring into your revision in this way which will help you to revise and learn the work.

You need to learn about:

- reasons for taking part in sport

  The little story on pages 34 and 35 might be one way of learning the reasons for taking part in sport. Start off by remembering that there are fourteen reasons, seven on each page: then you will at least know how many you are looking for.

- the seven factors of a balanced diet

  What are they and why do we need each factor?

- somatotype

  What are the categories and their relationship to sport?

- the heart – list

  Starting at the vena cava, trace the path of the blood as it circulates around the body. Be able to recognize the different parts on a diagram.

One way to help you remember facts about the heart and circulation is that 'atrium' starts with an **A**, so does 'above', so the atria are above the ventricles. 'Arteries' starts with an **A**, and they take blood away from the heart. If arteries take blood away from the atria then veins must bring blood to the ventricles, or visit the ventricles: **V** for visit, **V** for veins, and **V** for ventricles.

- the lungs – list

  Starting from the nasal passages, trace the path of oxygen as it circulates through the respiratory system and back again. Be able to recognize the different parts on a diagram.

- respiration and the chemical production of energy

- the mechanism for breathing

- EAR and the make-up of inhaled and exhaled air and the connection with EAR

- the principles of training

  Know the nine principles of training and how to apply them.

- Health Related Exercise

  Know the five aspects of HRE and be able to define them.

- skill fitness

  Know the six aspects of skill fitness and be able to explain how each might be used in a sporting activity.

  Remember they are as easy as ABC – that should start you off with the first three.

Applying things you know

Another way to revise can be by thinking about how things can be applied. Try this. When you are watching a sports programme on television (better still, when you are watching with a partner who is also taking the examination), look at the topics below and try to see how many of them are involved with what is going on and how well you can apply your knowledge. If you are working with a partner, ask each other questions, but work out the answers together if you wish.

- muscles
- bones
- joints
- flexibility
- heart and lungs
- safety
- drugs and sport.

You could also try applying your knowledge in the same way to what you are doing in your own sport or exercise.

In a similar way you could work with a partner and try to make up a scenario. You may have done some work on this in your sessions.

Ideas that fit together

There are things that go together, for example:
Effects of training and exercise

- immediate, longer term
- warm-up, main activity, cool-down
- interval, continuous, fartlek, circuit, weight
- aerobic and anaerobic
- flexion and extension
- adduction, abduction, rotation

You could explain one term, say interval training, then your partner has to name another, say circuit training, and then explain it.

A final point

Each part of the specification will almost certainly be examined, so do not miss bits out – and good luck!

Glossary

abduction   the action of a muscle causing a limb move outwards, away from the body

adduction   the action of a muscle causing a limb move in towards the body

adrenaline   a hormone that causes the heart rate to quicken

aerobic   'with oxygen'. If exercise is not too fast and is steady, the heart can supply all the oxygen the muscles need

aerobic respiration   production of energy in the body using oxygen

aesthetic qualities   the beauty in a performance

agility   the ability to change the position of the body quickly and to control the movement of the whole body

anabolic steroids   drugs, banned in sport, that mimic the male sex hormone testosterone and promote bone and muscle growth

anaemia   a deficiency of red blood cells causing breathlessness and a lack of energy

anaerobic   'without oxygen'. If exercise is done in short, fast bursts, the heart cannot supply blood and oxygen to the muscles as fast as the cells can use them

anaerobic respiration   production of energy in the body without using oxygen

analyse   examine in detail

anorexia nervosa   a chronic illness with loss of appetite and an obsessive desire to lose weight

antagonistic muscles   two muscles that work together to move a limb

artery   any blood vessel that carries blood away from the heart

asphyxia   a blockage in (or interruption to) **respiration**, preventing oxygen reaching the body tissues

athlete   an accomplished sportsperson

athlete's foot   an infection of the skin caused by a fungus. It causes dry flaky skin and itching between the toes

atrium   either of the two upper chambers of the heart into which blood passes from the veins. Blood passes from the atria into the **ventricles**

atrophy   muscle wastage (through age, illness, malnutrition or lack of use)

balance   the ability to retain the centre of mass (gravity) of the body above the base of support with reference to **static** (stationary) or **dynamic** (changing) conditions of movement, shape and orientation

ballistic   bouncing stretches which are not recommended

body composition   the percentage of body weight which is fat, muscle and bone

body mass index (BMI)   a measurement of body fatness using height and weight

bone structure   the thickness and weight of bones

bulimia nervosa   a condition in which the sufferer is obsessed with the fear of becoming fat. Bulimics eat vast amounts of food and then vomit or use laxatives to avoid putting on weight

calcium   a vital element for healthy bones, the best sources are milk, cheese and yoghurt

capillaries   microscopic blood vessels that link the **arteries** with the **veins**

carbohydrates   the body's main source of energy. Carbohydrates can be either starches or sugars

carbo-loading   a method of increasing **glycogen** levels in the body, partly by eating lots of carbohydrate-rich foods a day or two before an event (e.g. a marathon)

cardiac output   the amount of blood ejected from the heart in one minute

cardiovascular   relating to the heart and blood vessels

cardiovascular fitness   the fitness of the heart, blood and blood vessels and the ability to exercise the entire body for long periods of time

cartilage   gristle-like tissue. In humans, most cartilage changes into bone by adulthood

circuit training   a number of exercises set out so that you avoid exercising the same muscle group consecutively

circulatory system   the system that transports oxygenated blood and nutrients to the various parts of the body

continuous training   aerobic training, using exercise sessions with no rest intervals

contra-indicated exercises   those that go against what we know to be good practice

cool-down   a period of exercise after a main activity

co-ordination   the ability to use two or more body parts together

cramp   painful involuntary muscle contraction due to a build up of **lactic acid** in the muscle

dehydration   having an abnormally low water content in the body

diaphragm   a sheet of muscle and tough fibres that cuts off the chest region from the rest of the body cavity

diet   the food we eat

D.R.A.B.C.   **D**anger, **R**esponse, **A**irway, **B**reathing, **C**irculation

dynamic   changing or moving (especially if forceful or energetic)

ectomorph   a **somatotype** characterized by linearity (thinness)

elite athlete   sportsperson at the top of their profession

endomorph   a **somatotype** characterized by fatness

energy balance   taking in and using up an equal number of kilocalories

evaluate   assess the value of something

exercise   a form of physical activity done primarily to improve your **health** and physical fitness

expired air resuscitation (EAR)   artificial **respiration** by exhaling air into a victim's lungs (also called 'mouth-to-mouth' resuscitation)

extension   the action of a muscle causing a limb to straighten

fartlek   literally 'speedplay', **training** using jogging, sprints and rest intervals

feedback   give back information about a result

fitness   the ability to meet the demands of the environment

FITT   **F**requency, **I**ntensity, **T**ime, **T**ype

flexibility   the range of movement possible at a joint

flexion   the action of a muscle causing a limb to bend

glucose   a type of sugar found in carbohydrates

glycogen   the form in which carbohydrates are stored in the muscle and the liver

haemoglobin   the red, oxygen-carrying pigment in red blood cells

health   a state of complete mental, physical and social well-being, and not merely the absence of disease and infirmity

heart rate   number of times the heart beats each minute

hygiene   the practice of keeping clean and stopping the spread of germs

hypertrophy   muscle enlargement

intercostal muscles   muscles between the ribs

interval training   training using periods of work followed by rest intervals

isometric contraction   when a muscle contracts but stays in a fixed position, neither shortening nor lengthening, e.g. when pressing against a stationary object

isotonic contraction   when a muscle contracts and the muscle fibres shorten or lengthen, resulting in limb movement

joint   a place where two or more bones meet

lactic acid   a poison produced as a by-product of **anaerobic respiration**, can lead to stiffness and muscle **cramp**

lean body mass   total body weight less the weight of the fat in the body

ligaments   strong, elastic fibres that join bones together

mesomorph   a **somatotype** characterized by muscularity

metabolic rate   the speed at which we use up our energy

minerals   inorganic substances that our bodies need for a variety of functions

motor skills   our ability to move and co-ordinate our limbs well

muscle girth   the size around the muscle taken at the widest part when the muscle is flexed

muscle tone   voluntary muscles in a state of very slight tension, ready and waiting to be used

muscular endurance   the ability to use voluntary muscles many times without getting tired

muscular strength   the amount of force a muscle can exert against a resistance

nausea   feeling that you are going to be sick

notational analysis   recording a performance in writing (e.g. using a chart)

obese   describing someone who is abnormally fat. The condition is called obesity

observe   watch carefully (gather information)

optimum weight   most favourable weight for an individual

overfat   a way of saying you have more body fat than you should have

overload   the principle of **training** with enough intensity to improve your performance

overweight   having weight in excess of normal. Not harmful unless it becomes **obesity**

oxygen debt   the extra amount of oxygen needed to recover from **anaerobic** activity

perfect model   what a performance should look like at its very best

performance   how well a task is completed

posture   the way we hold our body when standing, sitting or walking

power   the ability to do strength performances quickly (power = strength × speed)

progression   starting slowly and gradually increasing the amount of exercise you do

proprioceptive neuromuscular facilitation (PNF)   assisted stretches using the help of a coach/teacher or training partner

proteins   chemicals contained in all living things, they are transported in the blood in the form of amino acids

psychological   to do with a person's state of mind or emotions

qualitative analysis   judgement based on our opinion of what we have observed

quantitative analysis   judgement based on facts

reaction time   the time between the presentation of a **stimulus** and the onset of movement

recovery rate   how long the **heart rate** takes to get back to normal

respiration   the process in which the body takes in oxygen and gives out carbon dioxide

reversibility   any changes that take place as a consequence of **training** (e.g. increased fitness) will be reversed when you stop training

RICE   **R**est, **I**ce, **C**ompression, **E**levation

rotation   the action of a muscle causing a limb turn round

scouts   people who look for new players for a team, or **observe** opposition teams

skill practice   a practice design to improve a particular skill

somatotype   body types (*see* **ectomorph, endomorph, mesomorph**)

specificity   you must do specific kinds of activity or exercise to build or improve specific body parts or skills

speed   the rate at which an individual is able to perform a movement or cover a distance

sports psychology   studying the mental approach of players to their sport

static stretches   easy stretches which are held for about 10–15 seconds, without straining

static   stationary, not moving

steroids   *see* **anabolic steroids**

stimulants   drugs that act on the central nervous system to make a person more alert. They include nicotine, caffeine, amphetamines and cocaine

stimulus   something that produces a response (e.g. the sound of the starter's pistol)

stroke volume   the volume of blood pumped out of the heart by each **ventricle** during one contraction

symptoms   what someone feels and can describe about an injury or illness

tactics   strategies to deal with a particular opposition, usually worked out in advance of a game

tendons   non-elastic fibres that attach muscles to bones

tidal volume   the amount of air breathed in or out of the lungs in one breath

training   a well-planned programme to improve performance, game ability, **motor skills** and physical fitness, using scientific principles

veins   blood vessels that carries blood towards the heart

ventricle   either of the two lower chambers of the heart that contract to force blood around the **circulatory system**

verrucae   a verruca is a type of skin disorder that can appear on the sole of the foot

vital capacity   the maximum amount of air that can be forcibly exhaled after breathing in as much as possible

vitamins   chemicals required by the body for good health, they can be either water soluble or fat soluble

VO₂ max.   the maximum amount of oxygen the body can take in

warm-up   a period of **exercise** to prepare for a main activity

weight training   using progressive resistance, either in weight lifted or number of times a weight is lifted